THAT'S THE
FORECAST !

THAT'S THE FORECAST !

The Best and Worst of Yorkshire Weather

Paul Hudson

GREAT NORTHERN

Great Northern Books
PO Box 213, Ilkley, LS29 9WS

First published 2005
Reprinted 2007

ISBN: 978 1 905080 13 7

The publishers acknowledge the assistance of Yorkshire Post Newspapers in providing the photographs for this book credited as YPN. Other photographs have been provided by viewers of *Look North* and have been credited wherever the name of the photographer is known. Cartoons by Stephen Abbey.

Design and layout: Richard Joy

Printed by
Quebecor Ibérica, Spain

British Cataloguing in Publication Data
A catalogue for this book is available in the British Library

Contents

(**Page 1**) Cumulonimbus cloud at Clayton West, near Huddersfield
(**Page 3**) Sunrise in Robin Hood's Bay *(Andrew Harker)*
(**This page**) Sunshine through the trees, Heaton Wood, Bradford *(Tony Fickes)*

Introduction

Since co-writing *Weather or Not* back in 2003 with my friend and ex-colleague Bob Rust, I have been amazed by the response, reinforcing my view that we are all truly obsessed with the weather. I so enjoyed writing the first book that I have been itching to write another, and so it came to pass during the spring and early summer of 2005. I did in fact think to myself during the book signings of winter 2003 that I should enjoy it because I couldn't think of how I would be able to write a second book on the same subject, at least not for many years, as I thought I had more or less covered all the material on weather available to me. But since then, our weather has continued to swing from one extreme to another, as Yorkshire's climate continues to change. On a much lighter note, there have been some memorable TV incidents both on and off screen. Incredibly, linked town names on the weather map each evening has produced more viewers' letters and e-mails than wrong forecasts ever did, which, believe you me, speaks volumes for the popularity of that part of the presentation!

One thing that has been introduced in the last two years on screen has been the viewer's picture each evening. This is nothing new to weather broadcasts over the years. However, the advent of digital photography and the internet has revolutionised the whole concept, with viewers sending pictures every day in the hope I will show them in the evening *Look North* broadcast, with an explanation of what unusual cloud or strange rainbow had been witnessed. Every day I receive numerous quality photographs of real, actual weather events, sometimes only an hour before transmission time.

It soon became apparent that such were the quality and diversity of the pictures that this would form the essence of a new book, together with the ever-popular good old-fashioned colour and black and white photographs of exciting weather events from the past. Although images of weather are the main thrust of this new book, I have combined them with the rather more serious subject of climate change in our region, plus, by popular demand, a few selected anecdotes from the lighter side of broadcasting on *Look North*!

Paul Hudson
July 2005

1.
Memorable
Moments

Memorable Moments

My first thoughts for this new book came to me whilst enjoying a winter break abroad last year. As sad as it may seem, there were some magnificent towering clouds in the sky that brightened up my morning (although my wife gets very bored with such excitement and understandably doesn't exhibit quite my enthusiasm for clouds). But what really got me thinking was the lush green cricket pitch that was only a stone's throw from the beach and hotel. I remembered just how big cricket used to be in my life before work and the family gradually took over – and just how big the weather is in my life now. There really is no getting away from it, whether I'm at work, at home, or on holiday!

Right from the start of my broadcasting career at the BBC, I would take every opportunity to mention Yorkshire County Cricket club in my forecasts. It was perfect from my point of view; I had a genuine interest in cricket, and it was obviously a very weather-sensitive sport. So I did go through a stage of giving a forecast for every home game of the season, come rain or shine. I came unstuck, as you will soon find out not for the first time, on the eve of a vitally important match at Headingley. I had forecast rain all day, and I couldn't see any chance of play being possible. Unfortunately for me, the forecast turned out to be completely wrong. The rain cleared by 10am, and the rest of the day was fine and dry. I later found out from one club official that the attendance was less than half what they expected, with ground receipts down by more than half – and I was directly blamed because of my lousy forecast the night before!

(Previous page) Rainbow above a field of oilseed rape between Masham and the A1. *(Bruce Greer)*

I now tend not to mention outdoor events if the forecast is poor; it is just not worth the hassle in case the forecast is wrong and it turns out to be a beautiful day. This is especially the case for country shows that are so heavily reliant on the revenue they generate. I have spoken to organisers who despair when country shows are washed out – especially since Foot and Mouth – and although the spring, summer and autumn of 2003 were beautiful, the summer of 2004 was appalling, leading to numerous events being postponed yet again. Honley Show is still in my book the unluckiest – having been washed out in June 2000, it was cancelled due to Foot and Mouth in 2001. Thankfully, although very wet under foot, June 2002 was most successful, but it must be heartbreaking for the organisers who see a whole year's work thrown away due to the elements.

There are occasions when show organisers are simply unfair in their criticism. The Lincolnshire Show of 2004 had poor attendance simply due to dreadful weather which affected the whole country at that time – in fact I thought that considering the heavy rain on the first day and gales on the second, the number of visitors was remarkably high. Looking back that was the first indication of just what a dreadful summer lay ahead with the deepest area of low pressure in June for sixty years. The forecasts that week were spot on – weather warnings were in force, and the wind and rain came right on cue. But for some reason the show organisers blamed my weather forecasts (note, not the weather) for being too pessimistic!

To be fair, forecasting for any outdoor event, or the coast and countryside, where people's livelihoods are at stake has always caused us immense problems. If on a Friday evening the forecast is good, then Mr and Mrs Smith will

head to Bridlington for a weekend break. If the forecast is wrong, they are very unhappy. It is not uncommon for me to come into work on a Monday morning and have messages of complaint on my answerphone. I remember on one occasion that it turned out a couple had nearly got divorced after spending a weekend in their caravan in Hornsea. I had apparently forecast a fine weekend, and it had done nothing but rain and drizzle, with sea fog thrown in for good measure. So they had sat in their caravan arguing all weekend and listening to the rain come down, as it can only do when you are in a caravan, and had come home early, clearly their relationship not in good shape. I hope they patched things up – I suppose a bad weather forecast on the divorce papers would certainly be a first!

We can also get stick from the tourist boards for, as they

Weather forecasts are crucial for country shows that are so heavily reliant on fine conditions to maximise revenue. Kilnsey Show in Upper Wharfedale had an especially bad day in August 1986 when the remnants of Hurricane Charlie hit Yorkshire. Up to three inches of rain fell in the Dales over the Bank Holiday weekend and at Kilnsey the River Wharfe covered the valley from side to side.
(Yorkshire Post Newspapers – YPN)

see it, stopping people making trips to the coast. If the weather turns out to be much better than we have forecast, then, so the theory goes, revenue at guest houses will be adversely affected because people will decide against making a trip out! So you can see, we do get stick from many directions!

If on a Friday evening the forecast is good, then Mr & Mrs Smith will head for Bridlington for a weekend break. If the forecast is wrong, they are very unhappy. Which category the spectators on the harbour wall fell into in December 2004 is open to conjecture but they certainly witnessed a dramatic spectacle. (Andy Prowse)

I remember on one famous occasion Bob Rust stated on his forecast that it always rained in Skegness. Oh Dear! It wasn't long before the Skegness Tourist Board wrote to Bob, blaming him for the lack of tourists visiting the area. Bob offered to come down to Skegness and do the weather live so that the viewers at home could see just how nice was the Lincolnshire resort. He set off on the long journey from Leeds a few days later and, much to the consternation of the Tourist Board, it rained all day long and the view of Skegness was awful. There was no-one on the beach and rain hammered down all through the forecast! But it has to be said that these days in summer are fairly rare, and in fact East Lincolnshire has one of the driest climates in Britain.

There are different levels of weather howlers and, although the Met Office will continue to get forecast detail wrong from time to time, it is now incredibly rare for it to miss an extreme weather event. Our dismal failure to predict the October storm of 1987 was no laughing matter, with lives lost and hundreds of millions of pounds worth of

damage suffered – although having said that I'm not sure what difference issuing such a forecast would have made to the damage sustained. Do we honestly think that people would have boarded up their houses and cut down unstable trees in advance? I very much doubt it. But it may have discouraged some people from venturing out that night, and so perhaps it may have prevented some of the lives lost.

On a much lesser scale, but very serious nonetheless, was the heavy snow and blizzards that caused chaos across Yorkshire at the end of January 1995. Heavy snow had in fact been forecast, but it came twelve hours earlier than envisaged and hit the rush hour in the afternoon as opposed to during the quiet small hours of the next morning. This was the worst forecasting failure in my time at the Met Office, and although forecasting is a collective job, it is invariably the man on the TV or radio who gets the stick.

The day the Met office got it badly wrong! This is the teatime rush hour in City Square, Leeds, in late January 1995. Rain had been forecast that night, but it turned out to be much heavier than anyone thought, and through a process known as evaporative cooling, turned to snow twelve hours early. It fell at a bad time with traffic queues preventing gritting teams from getting through. By 9pm that evening hundreds of motorists had become stranded, with abandoned cars littering the main roads and causing further obstacles. The next day more heavy snow fell, but then turned to rain and in the resulting thaw widespread flooding occurred during early February. *(YPN)*

The buck stopped with Darren Bett, now Broadcast Meteorologist with BBC1, who handled it brilliantly.

The same could not be said for the way the Met Office handled the October 1987 disaster. Incredibly, its PR machine (or lack of it) simply tried to make excuses, and took strength from technicalities in that it wasn't strictly a hurricane. It should just have held up its hand, explained what had happened and told the public that yes indeed we had got it badly wrong. Much has been learned since those dark days, and the Met Office was ready for the next 'biggy' to hit our shores, the Burns' Night storm of January 1990. This was forecast extremely well and our new warning system excelled.

Cricket calamities

Thankfully, since I began broadcasting on *Look North* back in November 1997 there has not been a fatal forecast error. However there have been plenty of embarrassments along the way, which thankfully I can laugh at now, but at the time, I can tell you, it didn't feel like fun. I remember one famous occasion when it was the eve of a test match at Headingley. England were playing South Africa and the forecast looked really good. To put it in context, the spring and early summer had been poor with frequent areas of low pressure that had led to showers or longer spells of rain. It was a revelation that on the eve of the test match, which was a sell out, high pressure would at last build from the southwest and give us our first spell of summery weather. So on the Wednesday morning at *Look North*, I offered to do a full five-day forecast live at Headingley to pass on the good news.

There I was at 6.30pm right at the top of the programme teasing ahead to the main weather at 6.50pm, saying something like "and don't forget to join me later because I've got some great news to tell". And so 6.50pm came, and Harry introduced me with words to the effect that "the whole of Yorkshire are going to like what Paul has to tell

us". Then it was my turn. By some cruel twist of fate that evening, a news story had not made it and so to fill the gap at the end of the programme I had something approaching three minutes on the weather. So you can imagine, I had really to stretch the forecast out, desperately trying to fill the time. When I had eventually finished, every single one of our viewers could have been under no illusion that summer was indeed on the way and the test match would bask in beautiful weather. In fact, in a further desperate effort to fill time I even illustrated how nice the weather would be, suggesting that there was absolutely no need to bring an umbrella or a coat.

And so the scene was set for a great first day at the test match. As is customary for every weather forecaster I know, the first thing that happens after waking up in a morning is to dive towards the nearest window to see what the sky looks like. I have to say that when I saw thick cloud I wasn't exactly thrilled. However, confident that it would break up, I got ready for work and drove into Leeds. It was 10.15am and, as I approached north Leeds, three big spots appeared on my windscreen. I hoped it was a bird with a hyperactive bladder, so I drove on. Then more drops, and more, until the wipers came on, and then I realised what was happening. It was raining. And I was less than two miles from Headingley itself. I couldn't believe it. I have to admit that for a split second I considered turning round and ringing in sick. But I thought, no, it's just a small passing shower and everything will be fine. By the time I had got to the BBC my wipers were on full. It was siling it down. So I trudged upstairs, went into the weather office, and turned on the TV to see all the covers were on at the ground. I looked at the radar and saw this huge line of rain that had obviously just decided to develop over Morecambe Bay and Lancashire (where else!). Then Richie Benaud, the cricket commentator, quietly said on TV, "Well, its not quite the forecast that I saw yesterday evening."

Not one to miss a trick, it had suddenly dawned on the lunchtime presenter, Peter Levy, that he had a golden opportunity to rub my face in it and promptly ordered me up to Headingley that lunchtime to do a live weather forecast. I thought to myself, "I'm dead meat! The members are going to have a field day." What's more I was dressed in my rather loud and sickly mustard yellow jacket that is not exactly designed for a quiet entrance. So I put my jacket on and went up to Headingley. Cruelly, the cameraman had positioned himself right in front oF the members' enclosure. I turned up to a mixture of leg pulling, some light-hearted and some not so light-hearted – as anyone who knows the members at Yorkshire County Cricket Club will vouchsafe. I remember one bloke who must have been 6 ft 4 in tall and built like a brick house came towards me absolutely drenched. Unfortunately he had believed my forecast and not bothered to bring his jumper, let alone his umbrella, and threatened to send me his dry cleaning bill.

I did my best on the lunchtime forecast, with audible jeers from the members' enclosure, and the customary light-hearted stick from my old sparring mate Peter Levy who suggested Mystic Meg could do a better job, and turned to go back to the studios. As I did, Andrew, the groundsman, shouted me from the wicket. The two umpires, Peter Willey and Ken Palmer, were having a conference in the middle with Andrew to try and decide when to take the covers off, and Andrew wanted my opinion. The members, who had suffered my forecast the night before, greeted this with howls of derision. I don't think it helped walking onto the wicket in my bright yellow jacket either, because I could clearly hear the mutterings from all round the place – very unforgiving with its full complement of 15,000 wet people!

When I got to the middle, Andrew introduced me to the umpires and promptly announced that I had a forecast that might help them. Now for those of you who don't know anything about cricket, Peter Willey can look very fierce and Ken Palmer is gruff and rather awkward. So I told them it would be a mistake to take the covers off; my radar suggested that there was another band of rain coming from Lancashire and therefore it would be prudent to keep the covers on. Peter Willey looked at me as though I had just landed from Mars. I can't really repeat what Ken Palmer said but, watering it down somewhat, he told me in no uncertain terms that he had stopped listening to weather forecasts fifteen years ago and wasn't about to start listening now and promptly ordered Andrew to remove the covers.

I trudged off head down, waiting for another barrage from the members' enclosure, when I heard something that rather confused me. As I approached the pavilion, ripples of applause broke out, followed by cheers. As I left the playing area, the applause got louder, with shouts of "Well done Paul!" And then it suddenly dawned on me. Everyone in the ground thought that I had told the umpires the weather would be fine and they should take the covers off. Little did they know! But I was forgiven, and I wasn't in any mood to start putting the record straight!

A second rather embarrassing moment regarding test match cricket occurred at the start of the International match with England playing the West Indies. Chris Hassell, chief executive at the time, called me on my mobile at about 9.30am on the morning of this crucial match. I was slightly overawed when Chris told me that Duncan Fletcher, the England coach, was stood next to him and wanted some advice on likely weather conditions. At Headingley, more than on any other ground in the country, the weather plays an enormous role in the final outcome of the match. The England coach and captain didn't know what to do if they won the toss – whether to bat or to bowl. So I gave Duncan Fletcher the full detailed forecast for the day's play. It was a dead certainty; it was dull and overcast now, and was likely to stay that way for the rest of the day. The atmosphere would be heavy and would favour bowlers not batters. So I said, confidently, "If you have the choice make sure you put the West Indies in to bat."

Thank goodness England lost the toss. Within an hour of play the cloud had broken up and after the luncheon interval there was not a cloud to be seen, with unbroken sunshine and temperatures in the mid-seventies. England won the test match in record time inside two days and the weather had indeed played a big role in the outcome. As is always the case I would like to take full credit for that, but, alas, Duncan Fletcher didn't have to use the weather information that I so confidently gave him. It is hardly surprising then that I haven't had any further telephone calls from the England cricket coach!

The Met Office

It often surprises people when they find out exactly who buys weather forecasts from the Met Office. Football groundsmen will want to know how much rainfall is likely, so they can save money on watering. In mid-winter they need to have forecast hourly temperatures; many have under-soil heating which is very expensive to use and has to be turned on days in advance so an early warning of air frost is crucial.

Coffee plantations are vulnerable to ground frost and temperature alerts will be issued to various companies. If the temperature across the Brazilian plantations drops sufficiently low then the crop can be ruined. This would cause a shortage of coffee and drive the price up, so if advance warning of this can be obtained one can buy more in the futures markets in anticipation of the price going higher.

Any fans of Formula 1 Grand Prix racing may be surprised to hear that Williams and McClarens bought forecasts from the Met Office when I worked in the International Forecast Unit in Bracknell. This was to help them decide which tyres to use – wet, wet and dry, or dry. This was often a very lonely job. Only one person staffed the Sunday shift at Bracknell, and we were responsible for all these worldwide forecasts.

I remember vividly that one of my first Sunday shifts happened to fall on the day of the Italian Grand Prix. It started at 2pm that afternoon and I had prepared the forecast, which looked dry at first, but a cold front was likely to move in from the northwest bringing rain across the circuit. My confidence was helped when I read the Italian Met Office's forecast which was going for rain as well. Unfortunately the cold front never got across the mountains to the north and west and it stayed dry. The race was lost because the driver had decided on the strength of the forecast that he would use wet and dry tyres whereas everyone else opted for dry tyres. Now that's pressure for you!

This illustrates how critical an accurate weather forecast can be, representing the difference in motor racing terms between winning millions or winning nothing. Despite getting some wrong, the fact that customers such as Williams and McClarens still buy forecasts from the Met Office is a huge vote of confidence.

While we are briefly talking about the Met Office headquarters, I can't resist a lovely little story from long ago. I was told it when on a long night shift at the headquarters, which was then called CFO (Central Forecasting Office). The Met Office has certainly had its fair share of dry, awkward characters. I put this down to the fact that forty years of night shifts can certainly take their toll, or perhaps most just get fed up of being hounded about what the weather is going to do. This happens whether you are on TV or not – word can certainly get around that there is a weather forecaster in town!

One evening during what had been a really hot weekend during Cowes Week, one of the world's largest yachting regattas that takes place around the Isle of Wight, one of the senior forecasters received a telephone call from what he thought was a member of the public. The line to the chief forecaster's bench is ex-directory so this was not

supposed to happen. The caller on the line claimed to be the Prime Minister of the time, a certain Ted Heath, who politely asked if the forecaster would care to offer him a forecast for Sunday since he was taking part in the race. "Pull the other one," came the reply, followed by a resounding slam of the phone back on the receiver. Seconds later the phone rang again. Again, the caller announced that he was the Prime Minister, only to get short shrift from the senior forecaster who again slammed the phone down with the words "Bugger off I'm busy!" Several minutes later the chief executive of the Met Office came on the line. "I've had a call from the Prime Minister's office," said the voice on the other end of the phone. "Just to warn you that the Prime Minister may ring this evening for a forecast for the big race tomorrow. Make sure it's accurate!" At which point, or so the story goes, the senior forecaster went a funny shade of white.

Look North

For the last three years *Look North* has been split into two separate versions – one for Hull with Peter Levy, and the other for Leeds with Christa Ackroyd and Harry Gration. In that short space of time there have been a few memorable occasions. Christa and I often like taking the Mickey out of each other. Most of the time the viewer I'm sure knows we are friends having a laugh, but sometimes it perhaps doesn't seem like that.

On one now famous evening when Harry was on holiday (I'm quite sure he's pleased at his timing!), Christa was interviewing a couple in Rotherham about their ten foot long python that had escaped and was on the loose. As the interview was coming to an end it became apparent, to much hilarity in the studio, that the husband had named the python after his wife. Thinking this was rather funny myself, I added, after Christa had handed over to me before the weather forecast, that they should have called the python after her! Unfortunately Christa then stopped me in full flow, asking the question "Why?" As always this was a live unplanned exchange and I really couldn't think of anything else to say other than, "Because it's big, fat and slimy!"

Linked Town Names

Here is a selection of what became known as 'linked town names', which formed a popular feature of Look North weather maps. In reality they covered villages and smaller settlements as well as towns and other place names. They taxed the ingenuity of viewers to link elements of each name in order to create a meaningful phrase.

To avoid making it too easy for readers who want to test their skills, the names below are not in the right order. For example, the solution to No 1 is 'Live and let live'. Turn to page 108 for the remaining solutions.

1. Anderby, Letwell, Liverton, Liversedge
2. Cold Kirby, Two Dales, Toulson, Catchgate, Sloley
3. Menthorpe, Ingleton, Aycliffe, Stubbins, Three Holes
4. Winton, Somersby, Somerby, Lose Hill, Youlgreave, Youlthorpe
5. Farnley, Thealby, Asenby, Eye, Seething, Asselby, Canwell
6. Ingrow, The Green, Isley Walton, Springthorpe, Airmyn
7. Acomb, Toft, Outwood, Fishlake, Waterton
8. Itteringham, Aisby, Great Givendale, Whirlow
9. Muckton, Roseworth, Fordon, York, Bushby, Horsegate
10. Beesby, Thearne, Wetwang, Hindolveston, Earswick
11. Catcliffe, The Green, Gotham, Haswell, Tongue End, York
12. Bordley, Butterwick, Dishforth, Anderby, Breadsall
13. Muggington, Acomb, Hotham, Coleby, Toft, Coleby
14. Duck Street, Spofforth, Waterside, Aby, Bacton
15. Coniston, Handale, Clough Foot, Anderby, Waitby
16. Norton, Gooderstone, Newsham, Newstead, Risby
17. Toft, Armthorpe, Long Riston, Lawkland, Theakston, Thealby
18. Gayton, Acomb, Watton, Daybrook
19. Monksthorpe, Key Green, Wetherby, Brassington
20. Dogley Lane, Wansford, Anderby, Manby, Whiston
21. Undercliffe, Bedlam, Redbourne, Aberford, The Green
22. Pannal, Anderby, Bell Busk, Peterborough, Tinkersley
23. Ryedale, Littlebeck, Redmire, Ingham, Hood Hill
24. Goodmanham, Ugthorpe, Thearne, Thealby, Theakston, Anderby, Badsworth, Lythe
25. Aby, Ingleton, Worthing, Intake, Theakston, Bushby, Two Dales, Handale, Isle of Axholme, Birdworth
26. Jacksdale, Thealby, Whitby, Road Green
27. Aby, Fallgate, Attercliffe, Thearne, Seamer, Partney
28. Ovenden, Reeth, Turnditch, Theakston, Pointon, Noblethorpe
29. Lingbob, Pinchbeck, The Green, Felixkirk
30. Acomb, Christchurch, Happisburgh, Happisburgh, Mastinmoor, Anderby, Newton, Yearlby, Aby.

Perhaps that was a little too much detail but I had to think of something, and anyway, the producer in the gallery laughed.

I continued with my forecast with the now famous Ackroyd thunderous look glaring down the other camera. Christa then decided that it would look funny if she crept out under my camera, so it would seem to the viewer that she had stormed out. This happened half way through the weather, and I was finding it so difficult not to laugh because all I could see was Christa's backside just beneath my weather camera! When I had finished the forecast I handed back to the stand-in presenter Ian White who compounded the whole thing by looking ashen to camera, next to Christa's now empty seat, and saying "Oh dear, Christa's left the studio. Good Night!" So what had seemed like a funny instantaneous reaction by Christa now looked like she had in fact walked out in disgust. To cap the whole thing, the next day I was at a weather conference at the Royal Armouries and so wouldn't be on screen, making it look as though I'd been sacked!

What amazed both Christa and myself was the reaction in the press. Granted there was no news around at the time, and certainly when there is no news any old story can make it big. Not only did the *Yorkshire Evening Post* run the story on page 2 with colour grabs of the programme the night before, but it also ended up in the *Star*, *Sun* and *The Mirror*, with a headline that read "TV fat spat!" Two phone calls followed, one from a friend of mine in Ireland saying it was in the newspaper there, and news had even got to the Bahamas where my best man works as deputy head at the local private school!

It was very soon after this 'fat slimy snake' incident that the linked town names on the weather map seemed to take off. Unashamedly pinched from YTV weather when they decided to drop it from their weather maps, and immeasurably improved, the idea was to choose if possible two or more town names across Yorkshire and Lincolnshire, parts of which would link to create a phrase of some sort of meaning. In the very early days, Hotham and Wetherby (Hot Weather) would be used on a hot day and perhaps Coniston Cold and Windy hill (Cold Wind) would be used

on a cold day. This was soon expanded to three or more names, each combination becoming more and more obscure as I struggled to keep this idea going, but I have to say I never repeated any combination in the three years that I was doing it. Pinchbeck, Mileham, Cockyard, and Luddenden Foot seemed to stump viewers one evening (this was supposed to be a set of imperial measurements – Inch, Mile, Yard and Foot).

One combination that very nearly caused acute embarrassment was the innocent trio of Legbourne, Lessington and Cattal. Before *Look North* goes on air, I try to look at the 'running order' of the programme to see which particular item is before the weather, as this helps me to prepare for any handover naturally designed to throw me off guard by Christa, Harry or Peter. In fact on this particular night the item before me was about a cat which had only two legs. Because this was the last item I naturally presumed that it was a funny story, so proceeded to put the town names that linked to make 'Legless Cat'. To my horror, live in the studio, the item wasn't funny at all. In fact it was apparent that the owner was really quite upset at the fact that the cat had only two legs and she was trying to make it walk again.

Thong, Bedlam, Clowne, Wigtwizzle – the list is endless. Unfortunately the new modern computer system that the BBC introduced in May 2005 has made creating such combinations extremely difficult because the town name itself is linked to the Met Office computer which only recognises larger towns and cities. As most of the interesting names are very small villages and hamlets, the idea has had to be dropped – much to the consternation of some viewers. As soon as I find a way of getting round this problem I will certainly look to bring it back again, I'm sure by popular demand!

Looking back we really did have some fun at times. On one occasion a local MP came into the studio who was campaigning for a ban on Page 3 topless models because of complaints from his constituents. This again unfortunately was the item leading into the weather, so I started the forecast that night by saying, "You have to remember that Page 3 will always have its knockers." On another occasion, it was the James Bond night at the National Museum of TV, Film and Photography in Bradford. Christa handed to me by saying, "How on earth do we get from James Bond to the weatherman?'" To which I replied, "Pussygalore!" Thankfully I have a very understanding boss.

On the Hull *Look North* programme, presented by the multitalented, multi-syruped Peter Levy who always has a girl on each arm, there has been many a hilarious moment. It is so difficult for me to highlight the best moments simply because at times anything goes and there have been so many of them. Viewers will remember Peter from doing *Look North* and Radio Leeds in West Yorkshire before he made his trip along the M62 a couple of years ago, and it was the lunchtime laughs which made a name for us both as long ago as 1997. On one evening, one of *Look North's* producers decided that he would like to propose live on air to his girlfriend. His name was David Prescott, son of the rather famous Deputy Prime Minister and Hull East MP, John Prescott. And of course, David wanted to do it during my weather broadcast.

That evening, David barged into the weather studio, proposed to his now lovely wife, Ros, and was promptly shunted off camera by myself worried that there would be no time left to finish my weather broadcast. To make light

Clearly I had not time to change my weather map, as I was all ready to start the forecast. There were only two things that I could do. I could either stand in front of the map for two minutes hoping no-one would see the names (a non-starter really!) or apologise in advance, which is what I did. Of course this didn't work because it only drew attention to what was on the weather map even more. So on with the forecast I went, and it was perfectly clear when the penny dropped with the main presenters because an audible gasp was heard. At the end of the forecast Christa had thunder written all over her face, but Harry saved the day, clearly wetting himself with laughter. This was a green light for one last line. "And there is another one I've missed that I could have used tonight," I said, "Stump Cross Caverns!" The owner, thankfully, saw the funny side of it.

Many evenings have been brightened by these simple town names on the weather map, and our region I think is blessed by some of the most unusual names in the country. Bag Enderby, Dog Dyke, Wasp's Nest, New York, Slack, Bottoms, of it at the end, I simply said, "If you are watching, my advice is don't do it, because David will end up looking like his Dad!" Well, it is the first time that something in my broadcasts has made it to the upper echelons of power. Rumour has it that the Deputy Prime Minister himself, aware that I was a civil servant working for the Met Office, threatened to flex his muscles and have me removed for such cheek! Some time later my wife and I were guests of David and his wife at their wedding, a splendid affair at Westminster Cathedral and later the Houses of Parliament. Although my comments were brought up twice during the speeches, I am pleased to report that much to my relief Mr Prescott and his wife Pauline very much saw the funny side of it all!

2.
Yorkshire Weather

Dawn of the Day

hen I began my career in the Met office, life as a forecaster meant working shifts. The operation at both Met Office headquarters and the local outstations had to be open 24 hours a day, 365 days a year, and so we all took our turn working nights. It quickly became clear that the end of the night shift, that is towards the dawn period, was often the most challenging – and not just because we had been up all

(Previous page) A fabulous bolt of fork lightning hits ground in Chesterfield – outside Yorkshire but in an area where many viewers receive Look North. The photographer commented, "I took a series of photos, but this one was taken almost accidentally, the flash and bang was so loud that I pressed the shutter release by accident." *(Nick Rhodes)*

night and were desperate for some sleep!

Local weather conditions can change really quite dramatically in the time just before or just after sunrise. In summer if the air is hot and unstable from the near continent it is quite common for the atmosphere to destabilise around dawn. This process is called cloud top cooling and caught me out on one occasion. I had just written and sent my weather script for local radio talking about a fine, warm and sunny morning followed by scattered afternoon thunderstorms. Suddenly I heard a very loud clap of thunder that nearly knocked me off my chair!

Dawn is also a critical time for mist and fog formation (as noted below). In short, getting the forecast right at this time was the most challenging job of the day.

(Left) Fog in the valley bottom, Dalby Forest, October 2004. The coldest temperatures are usually just before sunrise on a calm, clear night, and hence this is when mist and fog has the highest chance of forming. Here relatively warm, moist air has come into contact with the cold air at the valley bottom, which has formed partly in situ and possibly due to a Katabatic flow. A Katabatic breeze forms when air cools at the top of a hill faster than its surroundings and hence becomes denser and heavier. It then rolls down the side of the hill and collects at the valley bottom. Katabatic winds are common in the lower Dales. Another area that collects cooler air in this fashion is the Vale of York, probably one of the most common parts of the country for fog formation. Not only does it get a Katabatic drainage of cooler air from the Pennines but also from the North York Moors and the Yorkshire Wolds. *(Paul M. Woolverton)*

(**Above**) A cold January morning just as the sun rose at Askern Lake, near Doncaster. A frosty morning, with only small amounts of high cirrus cloud in the east creating a beautiful golden sunrise. Note also the ever increasing phenomena of aircraft contrails in the sky – it is rare these days to ever see a completely clear sky due to the inexorable rise in aeroplane traffic. These two aircraft were flying above 30,000ft almost due east into continental Europe. (*Clive Mitchell*)

(**Right**)   Hill fog in winter is not uncommon in Pennine areas. This picture was taken shortly after dawn in early February at Bolster Moor, Huddersfield. The moor is clearly on the edge of the thicker 'upslope stratus' cloud, which formed as warm air was forced up the western slopes of the Pennines. As it tries to continue on its journey, the air becomes drier and the fog or low cloud begins to disperse. (*Mark Mercer*)

(Above) This remarkable picture was taken one morning early in December from South Bay, Scarborough. Moist easterly winds from the North Sea usually lift over the land and condense into mist, low cloud and fog. However on this occasion radiation fog, which had developed overnight in the Vale of Pickering, began to drift over the cliffs at Holbeck Hill and towards Cayton Bay under the influence of a gentle westerly breeze. As the fog slowly descends the cliff edge, it becomes drier and warmer, leading to its evaporation. *(Jenny Tingay)*

(Left) The banks of the River Derwent at Thorganby Ings just after sunrise early one September morning. Autumn is often referred to as the season of mist and mellow fruitfulness; the longer nights allow temperatures to fall further than in the summer months, leading to a sharp increase in morning mists at this time of the year. The photographer commented at the time, "I think the combination of field, water, sun, reflection, mist, trees and sky have created a picture that I still find hard to believe is in England – how lucky are we to live in Yorkshire." *(Simon Mitcham)*

(*Above*) Another example of winter sunrise, this time taken early in February at Robin Hood's Bay. No doubt this sky led some residents of the Bay to predict poor weather ahead, from the saying 'Red sky at night shepherd's delight, red sky in the morning, shepherd's warning.' There is some scientific reasoning behind this piece of weather lore. An Atlantic weather front moving in from the west slopes forwards, and the first visual sign of a warm front is the thin, high cirrus cloud invading the sky as shown in this picture, scattering the sunlight and leaving the red end of the spectrum in the morning sky. If the cloud is indeed associated with a warm front, later that day cloud, wind and rain can be expected. (*Andrew Harker*)

(*Right*) A beautiful winter sunrise taken in Gledhow, Leeds. Atmospheric particles, including water droplets at the base of these stratocumulus clouds, cause the sunlight to scatter to the long end of the visible light spectrum. Red and orange have the longest wavelengths, and hence these are the colours that dominate the sky at dawn and dusk. (*C.R. Abbott*)

In the Clouds

Clouds were the prime source of our knowledge of the atmosphere before it was possible to measure its state using scientific instruments. Studying the clouds was an art that enabled people to make forecasts about the weather. This weather 'lore', based on centuries of experience, has been preserved in old sayings that we still use in conversation. Clouds can show the motion of air at high altitudes, give information about strong vertical winds and whether the atmosphere is stable or unstable. Many weather phenomena such as rain, snow or hail, thunder and tornadoes are formed inside clouds.

Clouds are, in fact, nothing more than water drops or ice particles, or put more simply, water in different forms. They can, however, exhibit a surprising variety of different shapes and they occur at all heights, from the surface of the earth to a height of 80km or more. Fog is simply a cloud that touches the ground. Between 6km and 10km are found the cirrus clouds that can reveal where the strongest jet streams are located. At 80km or more above the ground are found noctilucent clouds. Some clouds penetrate through the whole troposphere, the lowermost portion of the Earth's atmosphere where all our weather takes place. Such clouds are very often associated with bad weather, rain or snow, in connection with weather fronts or depressions.

Through the ages clouds have been classified by meteorologists and given Latin names, based on those devised by the British chemist Howard in 1803. Clouds are divided into ten main cloud groups, each of which contains different varieties. Before we knew how clouds formed, they were classified according to their shapes. For example, cirrus means 'a hair' and cumulus 'a pile'; sheet clouds were called stratus (meaning 'a layer'). Clouds that occupy the whole depth of the troposphere are called nimbus (meaning 'giant'), such as nimbostratus, stratus or cumulonimbus. Stratocumulus vesperalis form as leftovers from cumulonimbus clouds (vesperalis is derived from the Latin word vesper meaning 'evening').

Although the Latin descriptive names are used when reporting cloud formations, it is easier to discuss clouds in terms of how they actually form and the physical processes that are involved. The two main cloud types in this respect are layer clouds and convective clouds. Layer clouds form when a large volume of air is forced to move upwards and the air is stably stratified. This is generally the way clouds are formed along the warm front in a depression. Air is also forced upward when it is flowing across a mountain range and orographic clouds are formed. Cirrostratus and altostratus are examples of layer clouds in the upper and middle layers of the atmosphere.

On the other hand convection clouds form when the air is unstable and is moving upward in large bubbles. Such clouds get a cauliflower-like outline in contrast to the layer clouds that are smooth and without distinct contours and often cover the whole sky. The convective clouds include cumulus and cumulonimbus. Weak convection and mild turbulence gives rise to stratocumulus and altocumulus clouds. At a height of 6km to 10km cirrocumulus form when weak convection is present.

One of the most common questions I am asked is why are some clouds grey and some white? In fact the colour of a cloud depends on three things: the sun, how thick the cloud is, and where you are standing. If the cloud is between you and the sun and contains a lot of moisture, then less sunlight will shine through it, so it will look darker. You may have seen big tall cumulonimbus clouds that are very dark at the bottom. They are filled with moisture and can often bring heavy rain. But even if a cloud is thick, it may actually look white if you watch it with the sun to your back. The cloud reflects the sun's light and appears bright white.

You also may see cumulus clouds with the sun off to the side. Notice that the sides of the cloud facing the sun are bright white, and the sides away from the sun, especially the bottoms, are grey. Usually the opposite is true of high, thin cirrus clouds. They appear bright white when you see them in the direction of the sun since they don't block much sunlight.

If the sky is overcast with layers of stratus clouds, then it appears grey for the same reason that bases of heaped clouds do – most sunlight does not make it through the

cloud. Also a cloud may look white at first, but if a higher cloud moves in between it and the sun, the higher cloud casts a shadow onto the lower, which suddenly 'changes' from white to grey. In any case, watch out for clouds that are very dark and very tall. These can usually produce a lot of rain in a short time, so when you see them it would be a good idea to head indoors!

(*Above*) This is the best photograph of sea stratus that I think I have ever seen. It shows low cloud coming in across Robin Hood's Bay, as viewed from near Ravenscar. (*Denise Simpson*)

(*Right*) Clouds, sun and rain seen at their most moody in Upper Wharfedale, looking from the flanks of Great Whernside towards Kilnsey. Turner would surely have approved! (*Sebastian Wakefield*)

Digley Reservoir, Holmfirth, late in January with the Holme Moss transmitter mast just poking through the top of the clouds. The cloud is in fact often described in weather forecasts as hill fog, but is technically called upslope stratus. This is very common in winter, as moist air is blown in from the west, having picked up water droplets from the Irish Sea, and is lifted up the western side of the Pennines. The air then cools and condenses into this cloud, often shrouding the west side of the Pennines and the top of the hills. However, as it begins to descend the other side, it becomes warmer and drier, and the cloud begins to evaporate. This is a graphic illustration of the phenomena. The photographer noted, "I went over to the other side of the Pennines for the day, and the sun never appeared until I got back to the Holme valley." (Alistair Gibson)

Cumulus clouds are puffy clouds that sometimes look like pieces of floating cotton. These are frequently seen in Yorkshire during periods of fine weather, with high pressure across the country. The base of each cloud is often flat and may be only 1000ft (300m) above the ground. The top has rounded towers. When the top of the cumulus resembles the head of a cauliflower, it is called cumulus congestus or towering cumulus. These clouds grow vertically and they can develop into a giant cumulonimbus, or thunderstorm clouds.
(Kevin Kitching)

Quite the most remarkable cloud picture I think I have ever seen – the back edge of a clearing cold front with rich textured patterns on its underside lit by the setting sun. It was taken on the evening of 15th November 2004 from Halton looking just south-west of the city of Leeds.
(John Dolan)

(Above) An all too familiar sight in Yorkshire in summer – a thunderstorm cloud, or anvil cumulonimbus. It is no surprise that one of the best-known sayings about the British summer is 'four warm days and then a thunderstorm'. This particular storm cloud near Holme on Spalding Moor would have deposited torrential rain, accompanied by thunder, lightning and hail. A familiar Yorkshire summer story! The photographer described it as the best 'cunimb' he had ever seen in 72 years – including seven in the Met Office! *(J. Wilson)*

(Right) Anvil cumulonimbus, taken from Barton-upon-Humber looking northwards towards Yorkshire. This would have started its life as a small fair weather cumulus cloud, but with instability in the atmosphere caused by deep cold air aloft and heat at the surface it would have rapidly grown into the mother of all clouds. The top of the cloud is probably around 35,000 ft or more. At this height the anvil dome is formed, caused by very strong straight-line winds that are found at these altitudes and shear off the top of the cloud. The anvil shape can precede the main cloud structure for many miles. The generation of such a cumulonimbus is usually completed in less than an hour. *(Terry Clipson)*

A cloudburst and thunderstorm in August 2004. This month was very disturbed, as sub-tropical air led to flash flooding across the UK. In fact it was the wettest August since 1956, and in Sheffield the wettest since 1922. Here a well developed cumulonimbus can't hold on to its ice and water content anymore, and suddenly begins to dump its load over Huddersfield. The resulting torrential rain caused serious local flooding to some areas of West Yorkshire. The floodlights at the McCalpine stadium gives an idea of how dark it is, with the picture taken at around 7pm. *(Hayley Barrett)*

The same type of thunderstorm as in the photograph above, this time taken from Hall Bower cricket field, looking towards Castle Hill, Huddersfield. *(Nigel Rhodes)*

This is perhaps the most terrifying of clouds for any airline pilot. Associated with the biggest cloud of them all, the cumulonimbus, it depicts severe turbulence and is called mamma cloud. When witnessed, the observer would be able to see a slow rotation, taking place on the underside of the cloud. Airline pilots would be wise to avoid the area altogether, as the aircraft would be thrown around in the huge rotating currents of air. The International Weather Atlas describes mamma as 'seldom seen low to middle clouds associated with severe wind squalls, hail, heavy precipitation, tornadoes and thunderstorms.' The picture was taken at Altofts at 6.45pm on the evening of July 24th 2004, the formation only lasting a matter of minutes before dissipating. *(Steve Kirlow)*

Working on the Humber estuary at Immingham towing a ship, this photographer was in a good position to capture a scene that he had never previously encountered. Looking across to Hull, a classic sheet of hail and rain was being given up by the storm cloud above, the cumulonimbus being unable to hold its contents under pressure from gravity. The result – a dramatic deluge, together with ferocious squalls to test even the most experienced of mariners. *(Pete Elsom)*

(This page) Noctilucent clouds are most often seen at times close to the summer solstice, when they appear against the backdrop of deep evening twilights. They are high atmosphere cloud formations thought to be composed of small ice-coated particles; their precise nature remains a mystery. They form at very high altitudes – around 82 km above sea level – and are thus a quite separate phenomenon from normal weather or tropospheric cloud. This photograph was taken in Walkley, Sheffield, on 26th June 2004. The cloud caused much confusion and curiosity, appearing at around 2am in the morning when the sky should have been almost completely dark. *(James O'Neill)*

(Opposite) Nacreous clouds were seen on the morning and evening of 16 February 1996, and on the morning of 17 February. What was so unusual about this display was the colourful nature and the great extent of the clouds. Nacreous ('mother of pearl') clouds occur at an altitude of approximately 25-35 km – up to three times higher than the highest weather clouds – and are therefore high enough to be illuminated by sunlight long after local sunset. They form in the stratosphere when the temperature falls below -80 degrees C and are composed of ice particles. They normally appear as small, oval patches of pale, pastel-coloured cloud, the colours being caused by the reflection and refraction of sunlight through the ice crystals, similar to a rainbow. Occasionally seen from Scotland during the winter months, they are a once in a lifetime sighting further south.

Storm and Tempest

Thunderstorms are the most eye-catching of all types of weather and can often hit the headlines. They bring heavy rain, lightning, hail and, sometimes, tornadoes and waterspouts. During a thunderstorm the sky is dominated by towering cumulonimbus clouds which can reach heights of up to 19 km (12 miles). Inside each cloud, tremendous energy is generated and unleashed in the form of swirling upcurrents and spectacular bursts of high-voltage electricity. Large amounts of heat energy are released as water vapour first condenses and then freezes inside the cloud. This heat energy creates powerful rising air currents that swirl upwards, whilst at the same time cool descending air currents produce strong downdraughts below the storm. After the storm has spent its energy, the rising currents die away and the downdraughts break up the cloud. It is estimated that at any given moment nearly two thousand thunderstorms are in progress over the Earth's surface and lightning strikes the Earth one hundred times each second. There are about 45,000 thunderstorms daily and 16 million annually around the world! Tornadoes can sometimes develop near the boundary between the upcurrents and downdraughts in a thunderstorm cloud as described on page 44.

Hail is produced inside thunderstorms and is made of solid ice. Hailstones (see page 47 to 49) can grow to dangerous sizes before they fall but have to be at least 5 mm (0.2 in) across to be considered as hail. If the particles of opaque ice are smaller than this they are known as 'soft hail' (graupel or snow pellets). Hail occurs when ice pellets falling from the top of the cloud collect a film of moisture as they descend. The moisture freezes when the pellets are carried back to the top by upcurrents. As this process is repeated the hailstones grow in size and each trip through the cloud adds a new layer of ice. Once hailstones become heavy enough they will fall to the ground and can be a really dangerous weather hazard. Most are smaller than 2.5 cm (1 in) in diameter, but some can be as big as tennis balls or even grapefruit size. The largest can weigh a little under a kilo and fall at more than 50 metres per second. Hail storms can devastate entire fields of crops in a few minutes, flattening and bruising the growing plants.

(**Above**) Ominous clouds loom at Whitby, graphically silhouetting the abbey as viewed through the Whalebone Arch.

(**Right**) The abbey can also be seen on the skyline of this picture, taken at Sandsend beach, about 3km north of Whitby. There was a driving north-easterly blowing onshore, and the image shows a line squall over the town. (Carl Jacques)

(*Above*) Bridlington on 8th April 2005. This high sea was caused by a gale force northerly wind combined with one of the highest spring tides for years. Huge waves were reported along the coastline of Yorkshire and Lincolnshire, together with heavy snow showers. Earlier in the year similar conditions produced the highest tide in Hull for over thirty years. (*Josie Latus*)

(*Left*) Rough seas at Flamborough. The North Sea is commonly known as one of the roughest in the world. Big swells caused by Atlantic depressions can combine with a gale force northerly wind and high spring tides to create huge waves.

(**Above**) The River Humber is particularly prone to strong westerly winds, with funnelling occurring along the estuary, often leading to the bridge closing at least to high-sided vehicles. This particular picture was taken in October 1991, but more recently during one storm at the end of October 2000 a maximum gust of 99mph was recorded. Along with torrential rain, this led to structural damage and flooding across a wide area. (*YPN*)

(**Right**) Wind strength graphically illustrated on the Derwent dams, west of Sheffield, in January 2005 – traditionally the stormiest month of the year. The overflow water is being blown back up the dam wall and into the reservoir! Yorkshire was hit by three spells of severe gales in early 2005. Gusts reached 89 mph at Loftus, 87 mph at Leeming and 84 mph at Dishforth, causing much structural damage. (*Melvin Conway*)

Lightning Strikes

The chances of being struck by lightning are about one in three million according to the Met Office, higher than your chances of winning the jackpot in the Lotto, which is one in fourteen million! Mike Bellhouse from Leeds told us that one of his wife's colleagues was struck by lightning whilst walking in a park and was fortunate to walk away only a little tingly and shaken. Apparently less than three weeks later he won over £1 million on the Lotto!

(**Above**) A stunning picture of forked lightning striking Emley Moor mast. Sheet lightning was observed on the same evening, so called because it lights up the sky with a 'sheet' of light within the cloud. On this occasion the mast acted as a very convenient 'earth'. The most common thunderstorms occur in summer (as did this one) due to the heat of the day, but see below. (Ray Morris)

(**Left**) Emley Moor struck again! A bolt of lightning once again hit the mast, this time knocking BBC Television off air. This was during a more rare winter thunderstorm. These occur when cold polar air from the north tracks over the relatively warm Irish Sea, forcing the warmer sea air into rapid ascent. This process is exacerbated further as the air is pushed up over the Pennine hills, resulting in heavy rain, thunder and lightning. (Mick Brook)

(Right) Another superb example of fork lightning taken across Leeds city centre from Woodhouse at midday on the 3rd May 2005. Severe thunderstorms broke out widely across the area, with scores of properties flooded as 42mm of rain fell in the city in around an hour. Some of the very same properties that flooded in similar storms in August 2004 were hit again as the drains again failed to cope with the deluge. *(Gerry Devine)*

(Below) The consequences of a lightning strike can be devastating for those concerned. Firemen finish damping down the remains of the roof at a row of houses in Little Weighton, near Hull, in 1993. *(YPN)*

Tornadoes

Tornadoes have always been well documented. As early as 1165, a Yorkshire monk chronicled the appearance of the devil, describing the apparition as a black horse seen galloping across the Scarborough hillside. As conclusive evidence he cited deep hoof-prints running in a line across the dale. Modern historians have suggested the otherwise highly imaginative text may be a commentary on the manifestation of a tornado. In ancient drawings and illuminated manuscripts, tornadoes are often depicted with devils' heads.

On 26th September 1971 at around 4pm several startled Rotherham residents gawped at an oncoming 'ice cream cornet shaped cloud'. The tornado, with track estimated to be around twelve miles long, damaged houses in Rawmarsh. It was also reported that an Alsatian dog, complete with kennel, was carried over a fence and a garden, and that metal railings were sucked from the ground.

Tornadoes form near the boundary between the upcurrents and downdraughts in a thunderstorm cloud. A 'funnel cloud' develops first from the cloud base and this may then extend down to ground level. The destruction caused by tornadoes is due mainly to the violence of the winds. There is very low pressure at the centre of the vortex. If a tornado goes over a building it can explode outwards because of the sudden drop in pressure as the vortex passes over the building. Although they are usually less than 250 m across, they can travel a long way, sometimes more than 200 km (125 miles) across the land surface. They pick up material from the ground as they go, including cows, cats, dogs and other animals – including humans!

Most continents have regions where conditions for tornado formation are more likely to develop. On some remarkable occasions more than a hundred tornadoes have been recorded in a day, not only in the USA but also in the British Isles. In Britain on 21 November 1981 as many as 105 tornadoes broke out in five-and-a-half hours as a cold front crossed a comparatively small part of the country from north-west to south-east. Amazing as it may seem, the country with the highest number of reported tornadoes per unit area is England whose area corresponds roughly with Oklahoma, but many of the latter's tornadoes are more violent.

Some tornadoes form out to sea as strong waterspouts, which sometimes cross the coast, so a waterspout may become a tornado as the twisting funnel moves from land to sea (and vice-versa). A recent powerful and well-documented example is that of Selsey on the south coast of England on the night of 7th to 8th January 1998. When the waterspout made landfall, it carved a trail of damage a kilometre wide through the town as it damaged hundreds of buildings in less than ten minutes.

Lincolnshire suffered a tornado on 10th July 2004, here seen at Boston. The photographer ruefully explains: "There was a second twister that appeared straight after this one towards the north-west, but my batteries were flat on my camera." Such are the perils of digital photography! (Dave Smalley)

A disturbed spell of summer weather produced this tornado on 18th July 2004. The location is Potterhanworth, Lincolnshire, looking towards RAF Waddington. Within three minutes the column had essentially collapsed into itself, literally fading to misty cloud. *(Geoff Mountain)*

(*Above*) An August 2004 tornado – or to be correct a funnel cloud (since it hasn't in this picture at least hit land). This was a very disturbed month with sub-tropical air of high energy leading to numerous severe thunderstorms and reports of tornadoes The photograph was taken from Eldwick, near Bingley, looking towards Bradford. Manningham mills chimney can be seen on the right. (*Peter Smith*)

(*Left*) This tornado moved to the north of Cottingham at around 8pm on 23rd August 2004 in the direction of Beverley. The photographer commented, "I could see large amounts of debris being sucked up into the top of the swirling mass of cloud – at times it looked more like Oklahoma than East Yorkshire."
(*John Heard*)

Hailstones

One of the most notorious places for hail is the area in the USA from Texas to Montana, and from the foothills of the Rockies to the Mississippi River, known as "Hail Alley". Total hail damage each year in the US costs over $500 million and some incredibly large hailstones have been reported. The largest ever recorded in the US fell from a storm in Aurora, Nebraska on 22nd June 2003. It measured 17.8cm wide and 47.6cm in circumference! In this country we do not get such large hailstones but on 5th September 1958 at Horsham in West Sussex, stones of five ounces (142 grams) were reported. Hail can be very dangerous. On 20th April 1888, 246 people were killed in a hailstorm. Closer to home on 7th August 1996, six inches of hail fell in the suburbs of Sheffield with residents calling the local council to ask them to send out their snowploughs!

(*Above*)   Taken in Willingham by Stow, near Lincoln. As can be seen in the picture, some of the stones were larger than a pound coin. The photographer said, "The noise on my conservatory roof was horrendous – I thought we were under attack!" (*Phil Longstaff*)

(**Above**) Hail storm in Retford, north Nottinghamshire, in October 2004. (*Michael Ryves*)

(**Left**) Hailstones the size of marbles taken after a thunder-storm over Leven, East Yorkshire. (*John Goodlass*)

(*Above*) It would be easy to think that this was a scene from winter. But this picture was taken in early May 2005 in Hellifield, North Yorkshire. The photographer commented, "Spring seems to have sprung a leak – thunder and lightning was observed overhead, with hailstones the size of peas underfoot." *(Ken and Moira Hanning)*

(*Right*) Springer Spaniel Bess, enjoying the hail after a brief but violent thunderstorm in Lower Wyke, Bradford on 3rd May 2005. The owner's plants were battered to bits. *(Kath Barraclough)*

Water, water everywhere

Flooding has always affected Yorkshire and Lincolnshire, and there are numerous famous incidents that are well documented. In 1564 the Ouse Bridge was washed away as a great flood raced through York. Twelve houses built precariously on the structure were lost with their inhabitants. In February 1686 it was reported that a 'tempest' visited the villages of Kettlewell and Starbotton in Upper Wharfedale. According to the historical account the tempest struck with such violence that 'a hill on one side opened and cast up water into the air to the height of an ordinary steeple'. A number of houses were demolished, every stone been swept away into the raging torrent that was the River Wharfe.

In 1771, Northern England experienced the worst flooding on record. Half the town of Yarm was washed away and there was great loss of life throughout the region. On 4th July 1838, one of the most famous weather-related disasters struck Silkstone. At around 2pm in the afternoon a fierce storm erupted and for two hours torrential rain lashed the ground. Silkstone village was cut off by floodwaters for seven hours and at the nearby Huskar pit a catastrophe was unfolding. A swollen stream burst its banks, inundating the mineshaft and drowning twenty six children aged between seven and seventeen.

Floods are not in themselves meteorological events. The flood depends on lots of other things after the meteorology has done its business: geography, geology, soil-type, vegetation, land-use, drainage of farmland, drainage of settlements, building of roads and bridges, and water abstraction. They generally fall into three main categories – summer flash floods caused by severe thunderstorms; winter floods caused by heavy snow melt, especially as milder weather sets in during late winter and early spring; and general flooding caused by prolonged heavy rainfall, mainly in autumn and winter.

As we will find out later in the book, climate change means the occurrence and type of flooding is likely to alter. Summer flash floods will become more common as more warmth and energy becomes available to developing thunderstorms. Flooding due to heavy snow melt has already become rare in the last few years, whereas widespread autumn and winter flooding due to heavy prolonged rainfall will happen more often.

The photographs in this section are presented in chronological order. (Except where otherwise stated, all are courtesy Yorkshire Post Newspapers.)

(Opposite, top) At the start of the first week in July 1968, thunderstorms broke out across much of Yorkshire. Here in Cheapside, Bradford, subways and cellars were flooded and hailstones accumulated in drifts five feet deep. Around Harrogate windows were smashed, crops were ruined and hundreds of birds were killed, knocked out by hailstones the size of golf balls. Leeming in North Yorkshire reported 1.4 inches of rain in eight minutes. The rain actually deposited layers of sand that had been carried northwards from north Africa.

(Lower) A freak 33ft 6in tidal surge caused massive flooding in Hull city centre on the 28th and 29th September 1969. Scores of shops, offices, factories and warehouses in the Old Town were inundated, as seen here in Whitefriargate. Water engulfed the Humber Street fruit market in minutes, with little time for evasion. Two electricity transformers caught fire due to water penetration and Humber ferry sailings were cancelled. The nearby village of Paull was marooned and thousands of acres of farmland were swamped. On the Humber ten miles upstream, the river gauge showed an all time high tide of 25ft 9in.

(Above) June 1982 turned out to be a very stormy month. On June 1st, an inch of rain fell in just twenty-five minutes across Yorkshire during a cloudburst, followed the next day by another two inches in one hour as the county continued to be affected by severe thunderstorms. Many homes and businesses were affected by flash flooding, including this house in Scott Hall Road, Leeds, where Elaine Clavane (standing in the doorway) is being helped by neighbours to keep the water at bay. On June 3rd a house in Rotherham burst into flames having been struck by lightning, and a golfer in Sheffield had a lucky escape when a bolt of lightning threw him six feet into the air. On June 5th, one person was killed in Shipley and another on Ilkley Moor as lightning struck once more.

(Opposite) There is more than a touch of irony about the sign still on display on Denby Dale Road, Wakefield, following a local cloudburst in June 1983. Wading through the water is Lisa Broadbent.

(*Above*) Flash floods occurred due to torrential rain on 21st March 1981, with five inches recorded at one weather station in Snowdonia. This same band of rain moved northwards across Yorkshire, melting the winter's snow and causing flooding on many of the region's rivers including the Ouse at York. Among those virtually marooned was Elizabeth Robinson in Marygate, who is receiving her shopping by canoe.

(*Opposite*) The River Ure, whose source is high in Wensleydale, rises and falls rapidly. Boroughbridge has long suffered at the hands of the river, and early January 1982 – when 'floods volunteer' Noel Jorgensen was delivering milk by boat – was no exception. The seeds for the terrible flood were sown in December 1981, which turned out to be one of the worst Decembers of the century. By lunchtime on 14th December, twenty inches of snow was reported. On the night of the 18th, Bramham on the A1 near Leeds reported a record minimum temperature of -16C (2.7F), together with a foot of lying snow. Early in the new year a rapid thaw of lying snow, feet deep in Wensleydale, together with heavy rainfall caused the fastest rise in the river network since 1947.

WATER, WATER EVERYWHERE **55**

(Opposite) The January 1982 floods also inevitably affected York. Sandbags can only do so much and so a rabbit is being taken to drier quarters.

(This page) The prospects for Italian Ice Cream sales don't look good as mounted police from Harrogate patrol Tower Street, York, during January 1982.

(*Above*) The face of James Brazier says it all as cleaning-up oper-
ations start in his flood-damaged home in Hetherton Street, York.

(*Opposite, top*) Floodwater knows no stopping and with absolute
inevitability the January 1982 floods moved down-river from York
to embrace Cawood. Shopkeepers Mr & Mrs Lambert wade out of
their premises in High Street.

(*Lower*) Selby was the next town to suffer, and conditions were
being made infinitely worse by the fact that the floodwater turned
to ice.

(*Above*) February 1991 was another very cold month. Strong easterly winds from Siberia brought continuous snow across Yorkshire, with a level 18.5 inches recorded at the Met Office site at Bingley. Some villages in the Yorkshire Dales were cut off for days. But the cold snap was short lived, and two weeks later mild Atlantic air together with heavy rain caused rapid melting of snow, resulting in an all too familiar scene along the River Ure in Boroughbridge. In Fishergate many cars were totally submerged and a rowing boat once again became the favoured mode of transport.

(*Opposite*) The River Ouse in York in March 1999. Six Inches of rain fell over the weekend of 6th and 7th March which, coupled with melting snow over the hills, caused major flooding in the Derwent valley, and to a lesser extent in York. In fact such is the regularity of flooding at the King's Arms pub in York that it never made the news, as Stamford Bridge, Malton and Norton took the headlines with the worst flooding on the River Derwent since 1931.

The Derwent valley in North Yorkshire suffered two catastrophic floods within eighteen months of each other, each the result of two very different weather types. The floods of March 1999 were caused by exceptionally heavy and persistent rainfall over the moors. A low pressure system over the North Sea became blocked and fronts moved east to west between February 28th and March 9th, bringing first snow and then rain so that melting snow added to the run-off. Church Houses in Farndale had over 250 mm (10 inches) of rain between 28th February and 11th March, and other stations recorded similar figures. Rainfall of this intensity and duration is a very rare event – it would be expected to happen only once in a thousand years. The normal level of the Derwent at Malton is 14.52 metres above sea level, and it rose to 18.90 on the 8th March – 4.38 metres or 14ft 4ins above normal. It has quite often risen more than 12ft in the past – in 1930, 1947, 1960, 1963 and 1982 – and in 1931, said to be the worst flood in Malton's history, the level reached 18.70 metres.

So 1999 was, it seems, the biggest flood ever recorded.

The floods of November 2000 were unique in that snowmelt was not a consideration. Following a wet spring and summer, the water table was already very high. October suffered exceptional rainfall, with torrential downpours at the end of the month leading to the Derwent bursting its banks in exactly the same areas as it had done the previous year.

The following photographs are all of the 1999 floods.

(*Above*) A dinghy comes into its own in the main street of Norton, effectively the part of Malton on the east side of the river.

(*Opposite, top*) Aerial view of Malton town centre, with only small sections of the main road and railway above the level of the flood-waters.

(*Lower*) Flooded streets and gardens in Malton.

(*Above*) Stamford Bridge, lower down the Derwent, fared no better than Malton. Just visible at top right is the upper part of the bridge carrying the main road over the river.

(*Left*) It was not a happy time at Stamford Bridge for the owners of these mobile homes. Many of the 'homes' looked as if they were about to float down river.

(**Above**) Even when the floods started to recede, the misery was not over. Residents try to return to their homes at Norton to begin the huge clean-up operation.

(**Right**) Moving on from 1999, the year 2004 brought the wettest August in South Yorkshire since 1922. Localised flooding was fairly common through the month due to severe thunderstorms that resulted in near monsoon conditions at times. Here in Wath upon Dearne the locals certainly seem to be enjoying their new outdoor swimming pool! (*Robert McGibbon*)

Light
Fantastic

Rainbows

The idea that a pot of gold can be found at the rainbow's end originated somewhere in old Europe. In Silesia, an obscure area of eastern Europe, it was said that the angels put the gold there and that only a nude man could obtain the prize! The legends of many cultures see the rainbow as a kind of bridge between heaven and earth. One of the most beautiful sights in nature, the rainbow has become in western culture a symbol of renewed hope; something lucky to look upon. To Iranian Moslems, even the brilliance of the colours in a rainbow has significance. A prominent green means abundance, red means war and yellow brings death. The Arawak Indians of South America recognise the rainbow as a fortunate sign if it is seen over the ocean, while tribes in north-eastern Siberia see it as the tongue of the sun. The North American Catawba Indians of the south-east and the Tlingit of the north-west both regard it as the bridge between the living and the dead.

Throughout time, people have been fascinated with rainbows. Their arched splashes of colour have been the subject of songs and poems, stories and mythology. In the Bible, the rainbow is seen as a sign of God's promises, and most of us are familiar with the legend of the pot of gold at the end of the rainbow. What makes rainbows so mysterious is this simple but often puzzling fact that they are light. You can't touch them. You can't reach around behind them. They exist only in the eyes and sometimes the photographs of the people who see them.

Rainbows occur when sunlight falls upon raindrops, which act as tiny prisms. This causes the constituent colours of sunlight to leave at slightly different angles leading to a primary rainbow of seven colours: red, orange, yellow, green, blue, indigo and violet. The sun is

As good a rainbow as you will ever see. Light perfectly refracted though raindrops from a heavy downpour in Barton Upon Humber lead to a beautifully structured rainbow. *(Terry Clipson)*

always behind you as you face the rainbow. The higher the sun the flatter the rainbow will be and, when the sun rises higher than 42 degrees above the horizon, the rainbow will disappear.

Another larger bow is often seen outside the primary rainbow and parallel to it. This secondary rainbow is produced in a similar way, but the sun's light is reflected twice before emerging from the raindrop. For this reason, the colour sequence is reversed with red on the inside edge. And because there is a loss of light with each reflection, it is not as bright as the primary rainbow. The region between the two bows is comparatively dark, for it lacks entirely both the once and the twice reflected rays. There is theoretical evidence for a tertiary rainbow, but it would be so faint as to be rarely seen in nature.

Did you know you can forecast the weather by the colours

Changeable weather in April, with heavy showers interspersed with sunshine, can lead to an abundance of rainbows at this time of the year, as sunlight is split into its constituent colours. This picture was taken from Storiths, above Bolton Abbey, looking towards Riddings Hill and the Strid. *(Alan Chandler)*

in a rainbow? Well, according to weather lore, you can:
Green is the predominant colour – expect more rain.
Red means wind and rain.
Blue means clearing.
If it only shows red and yellow, expect fair weather.
If the rainbow is broken in several places, or only half is visible, expect more rain for the next two to three days.

I have to say I have not yet tried this myself, but I will certainly be checking the next time I see a rainbow!

(This page, top) A Boxing Day rainbow, photographed at Bridlington harbour in 2004. Note the secondary rainbow at top right. *(Pauline Taylor)*

(Left) A heavy shower passes through Wharfedale, with the briefest of sunny spells leading to a rainbow along the banks of the River Wharfe between Conistone and Grassington. *(Bob Sandy)*

On 13th July 2004 I was inundated with e-mails describing an upside-down rainbow that was clearly visible across South Yorkshire and North Nottinghamshire. Clearly this is a rare phenomena – most viewers who saw it had never seen one before. The technical name for an upside-down rainbow is a circumzenithal arc. It arises from refraction through ice crystals, as opposed to water droplets, and hence is seen much higher in the sky where the air is cold enough to sustain ice. *(Chris Simpson)*

Auroras

The Northern Lights, or aurora borealis as they are called in the Northern Hemisphere (aurora australis in the Southern Hemisphere), are a glow of green, yellow, red or even blue light that looks a little like bright curtains waving in the breeze. Usually, only people who live very far north or south of the equator see this display, but quite rarely the Northern Lights are visible here in Yorkshire.

An aurora happens when particles from the sun cause the earth's upper atmosphere to act like a big neon sign. In a neon sign, electric current runs through a wire into a glass tube filled with gas to make different colours of light, the colour being dependent on the particular gas. The same thing can happen high above the Earth. Electrically charged particles speeding away from the sun (called the 'solar wind') are captured by the Earth's magnetic field and then collide with atmospheric gases. Different gases give off different coloured light. Since the Earth's magnetic field directs the charged particles towards the north and south poles, the colours are usually most vivid there. However, sometimes the sun can release big bursts of energy. When these huge concentrations of charged particles reach Earth, auroras can be visible much further away from the poles, in fact right here in Yorkshire.

The Northern Lights have been the subject of speculation, myth and scientific study throughout history. Indigenous people in Canada and the northern USA had many legends to explain the lights. One legend says the souls of departed friends were lighting torches to guide those who followed. Another describes a great hole in the sky through which souls pass from this world to the next. Auroras were commonly associated with dancing in Norway, where inhabitants believed that they were old maids, dancing and waving. Most people were afraid of the lights. Children would be brought inside when the mystifying flames of auroras spread across the heavens, for the lights could descend and cut their heads off.

Thus, in many places the Northern Lights were a threat to people's lives and health. In many areas in the Nordic countries it was widely believed they were a vengeful force that killed those who mocked it. The mythological role of the aurora was important in religion. Many believed it was a message from the creator. Flaming auroras reminded people that their creator still cared for them. An old tale from the Nordic countries said that 'God is angry when the aurora flames'. It was a common interpretation during medieval times that the Northern Lights were an omen of war, or disasters or plagues. It was concluded that many serious disasters were caused by the aurora.

Although auroras were common occurrences to northern peoples, the occasional aurora seen in central and southern Europe created panic. Greek and Roman philosophers believed the sky was opening and spewing forth flame and smoke. In early times, people detected major fires by the light reflected from the evening clouds. When an aurora made an uncommon appearance in southern latitudes, troops rushed to neighbouring cities to help with what appeared to be a major conflagration. In the Middle Ages, Europeans went from hysteria to hallucination. They saw vast armies of angels clashing in the sky, and tens of thousands of peasants across Europe joined pilgrimages in hope of saving the world from the approaching Armageddon.

Science also had its opinions about the aurora. Some scientists speculated that the force of ice and glaciers produced flame, while others thought that vast ice belts reflected the sun's light into the evening sky. Active research began in the seventeenth century when Pierre Gassendi, a mathematician and philosopher, named the lights after Aurora, the Romans' rosy-fingered Goddess of Dawn, whose job was to usher in the rising sun.

The Northern Lights, seen on the A66 just outside Yorkshire on Bowes Moor on 21st January 2005. *(Mike Kenyon)*

(Opposite) Two spectacular pictures of an aurora borealis at Holme on Spalding Moor, 31st October 2003. *(David Chesmore)*

(This page) The Northern Lights captured over Skipton on 9th Novmber 2004. Although not as detailed as the photographer would have liked, there is clearly visible a reddish hue over the green/blue coloured sky on an otherwise moonless pitch black winter's night. *(Andrew C. Walker)*

Winter Wonderland

t is a sad fact for many of us that as our climate continues to warm, snow will become increasingly rare. Looking back through the archives, it is obvious – without having to study any weather data – that our climate was very much colder in the past. Many of Yorkshire's rivers used to regularly freeze over, and villagers across the Dales would as a matter of routine stock up the larder in autumn in anticipation of being cut off at least for a time from the outside world. The winters of 1946/47 and 1962/1963 are well documented and remembered by people who lived through Siberian conditions that lasted for weeks on end. I am often amazed when I look at pictures from the last really severe winter in early 1963. Photographs of snow piled to the top of road signs, barges trapped in pack ice on the River Hull and cars buried so deep in snow that only their roofs are visible seem barely credible now, and yet that was only just over forty years ago.

Although we are likely to see much milder winters in the

years to come, that does not mean that we won't be sur-prised by another very harsh winter in future years. In fact it is worth remembering that continental Europe had a severe winter during early 2005, and we were often very close to being affected by their cold and snow at the same time. And as we shall see later in the book, global warming may have some surprises up its sleeve, with some scientists believing that in fact our climate may turn very much colder.

The photographs on pages 74 to 78 look at past winters.

(*Opposite*)   The main road between Hebden Bridge and Keighley, virtually impassable at Pecket Well during harsh weather conditions in February 1969. Until the end of the 1980s this road regularly became blocked in winter but nowadays prolonged snowfall that lasts more than a day or two is very rare. (*YPN*)

(*This page*)   Prior to the building of the M62, it was a common sight to see lorries snowed up at Marsden waiting for the road over the Standedge pass to be reopened. This scene dates from February 1958. Pictures like this remind me of just how different the climate is now compared with only fifty years ago. Such scenes were common each and every winter back then, but now would be a very rare event indeed. (*YPN*)

(**Opposite, top**) The main York to Bridlington road across the top of the Wolds is notorious for snow problems. Motorists near Fridaythorpe are in difficulty in December 1968. Barely a year used to go by without most roads in this area being impassable at some time during the winter. The main culprit would be an east or north-easterly wind straight from Russia in January or February, bringing showers or longer periods of snow for days and sometimes weeks. Snowploughs would begin a circular route clearing the roads, only to return at the end of the day and find the snow had blown in from the fields making the road impassable once more. (YPN)

(**Lower**) Motorists marooned by drifting snow at Grindale, north of Bridlington, in January 1960 wave to a helicopter bringing emergency supplies. Incredibly only days later temperatures almost reached 17C (63F) across the UK proving that even back then the weather wasn't always relentlessly cold! (YPN)

(**This page**) Extreme cold in January 1983 caused many burst water mains. Residents in York Road, Leeds, had to rely on stand-pipes. (YPN)

(Opposite, top) A rare sight these days, as reputedly the last remaining horse-drawn snowplough in West Yorkshire clears the streets of Roundhay, Leeds, in January 1987. Siberian air affected Yorkshire for much of the month, with maximum temperatures on January 12th remaining below freezing. The cold blast lasted fourteen days, with most Pennine routes impassable. *(YPN)*

(Lower) Spring Gardens, Harewood, failed to live up to its name in 1990 as snow fell heavily in December on two days – the 8th and then again on the 18th. However, scenes like this were the exception to the rule throughout the year, as much of the winter turned out to be exceptionally mild. In fact February was the warmest on record, with 17C (63F) recorded on the 23rd. This trend of mild winters continued throughout the 1990s and into the new millennium. *(YPN)*

(This page) Snow soon cripples public transport, although generally the trains do get through rather better than some motorists. A good covering of the 'white stuff' carpets the platform at Harrogate station as passengers wait patiently. *(YPN)*

(*Above*) Snow on the coast can look superb as seen here at Scarborough with another snowstorm about to head in from the north. The east coast is prone to snow showers when cold northerly air pushes southwards from the Arctic. The contrast between the icy cold air and the relatively warm sea often generates very heavy showers, which run in along the coast one after another and sometimes for days. Substantial snowfall can result and, as the northerly wind is usually strong, drifting can cause major travel disruption not only to coastal towns but also to the North York Moors to the east. During the winters of 1963 and 1947, the bitter east to north-east wind generated many feet of snow in these areas.
(*Abigail & Hannah Durrant – aged 10 and 8))*

(*Lower*) Another fine view of Scarborough in winter, with the snow-covered Floral Hall in the foreground.

In recent years most of our snow has fallen near the coast in outbreaks of polar air from the north, mostly in the form of heavy
snow showers. At times they can be sufficiently heavy to cover the
ground at sea level, as seen here at the Humber Bridge.
(David Dalton)

(*Opposite*) Hoar frost deposited on trees in Judy Woods, Wyke. This forms as the air cools and water condenses onto the tree when the air temperature is below freezing. If the moisture forms when air temperatures are above freezing, it is commonly referred to as dew. Hoar frost looks very different from frozen dew, which is dew that has frozen after it has formed. Frozen dew resembles frozen water droplets, while hoar frost is a delicate icy structure. The different types of frosts are very important to motorists, who need to know when there are icy patches on the roads. (*M. Kitson*)

(*This page*) Large flakes of wet snow occur when the temperature is above freezing, say one or two degrees above zero. In these circumstances conditions become very marginal as to whether the precipitation falls as rain or snow. Overnight wet snow has settled on this wet tree, and then frozen as skies cleared around dawn. As pretty as this scene looks, this type of snow accretion can cause major problems for electricity companies. Overhead cables can be pulled down under the weight of snow and ice, leading to power cuts.

The Day's End

As the sun sets, its light travels at a much lower angle. The sun therefore shines through the lower atmosphere, which contains dust, salt, smoke and pollution. These particles scatter away some of the shorter wavelengths of light (the violets and blues), leaving only the longer wavelengths (the oranges and reds.) That is why many sunsets are orange. Where the air is cleaner, as in mountain regions, the sunsets will be white or yellow. When the concentration of particles is especially heavy, all the shorter wavelengths of light will be completely scattered away, and the sunsets will be very red. You often see a red sunset at the seashore because there are so many salt particles in the air over the ocean. Volcanic ash can scatter most of the blue light away too. After the eruptions of Mount St. Helens in Washington State in 1980 and Mount Pinatubo in the Phillipines in 1994, the ash drifting through the air turned sunsets around the world more red than usual.

(*Opposite*) A spectacular sunset from Sutton Bank, looking west across the Vale of York, late February 2005. The dying sunlight seems to shine through a gap in the stratocumulus cloud, which creates some kind of diffraction effect on the light, dispersing it in many directions. (*Anne Cope*)

(*This page, top*) The sun sets on another beautiful day in Bradford, throwing St Mary's Church, Wyke, into a distinctive sil-houette. (*M. Kitson*)

(*Right*) A strikingly colourful sunset at Mansfield Woodhouse, Nottinghamshire, on 30th December 2004. (*C.R. Abbott*)

(Opposite) If you enjoy sunsets and sunrises, living along the Humber estuary must be one of the best places in the country to see them. Spectacular sunrises in the east are often followed on a fine day by equally spectacular sunsets in the west. What makes the Humber so special is not just that it lies east-west so the sun sets and rises over water. It is the combination of the heavy industry along its banks creating particles of pollution, together with salt particles from the sea, which leads to heavy scattering of the light leaving reds and oranges of the visible light spectrum.

(This page) A Spurn Point sunset, early December 2000. The sun is beautifully captured setting into cirrus ice cloud behind the lighthouse. The yellow glow is an indication of clean, pollutant free air.

(*This page, top*) The beautiful Humber again! – sunset at Brough Haven. (*Keith R. Wilson*)

(*Lower*) Lincoln windmill at sunset. Most of the cloud has dissipated as the sun's strength weakens, but the small area of stratocumulus remains as the sun sinks ever closer to the horizon. (*M. Kitson*)

(*Opposite*) A magnificent sunset in Grimsby, with a stunning pinky red glow on the underside of altocumulus cloud reflecting in a calm Humber estuary.

3.
Climate Change
in Yorkshire

Climate Change in Yorkshire

Yorkshire's and Lincolnshire's weather is likely to continue to change. Summer's are getting warmer, but storms may become more intense. With heavier and more persistent rainfall in autumn and winter, floods will become more frequent, winds may become stronger and snow increasingly rare.

Mean Earth temperatures are rising, as is the concentration of Carbon Dioxide in the atmosphere. Carbon Dioxide (CO_2) is critically important to us; it is known to cause warming of the Earth's atmosphere, but without some CO_2 life would struggle to exist on earth. Devoid of this natural level of CO_2 our planet would see temperatures around 20C lower than is currently the case.

It must not be forgotten that our climate has changed before. A look at the temperatures over thousands of years shows cyclical change through the ages. The Vikings colonised Greenland during a warm period in the Earth's history and vines were common as far north as Knaresborough. However our climate has also changed in the past to become much colder and the 1700s and 1800s were famous for their harsh winters when rivers across the country regularly froze over. Indeed as recently as the 1960s and '70s scientists believed that we were slipping into another cold period, such were the cold winters we were experiencing and the dismally cold and wet summers that followed. But that now seems such a long time ago, and the 1990s and early part of the twenty-first century have seen a warming trend that cannot be explained by natural phenomena alone. In fact all the ten warmest years globally have occurred in the thirteen years since 1990, including each year since 1997.

(Previous page) Water vapour from the cooling towers at Ferrybridge power station rises high in the sky, indicating an unstable atmosphere. For me, this picture tells its own worrying story. I can't help but somehow link the fiery evening sky with the invisible polluter from the power station, Carbon Dioxide, which will pump out its gas 24 hours a day, 365 days a year, feeding the modern day monster – climate change. *(Richard Poskitt)*

The science as far as I am concerned is indisputable; in fact the only thing that surprises me when it comes to climate change is that there is any debate about it all. Put simply, the concentration of CO_2 in our atmosphere, a gas that is known to cause atmospheric warming, has recently been recorded at 380 parts per million (ppm) at the Hawaii observatory, USA. Carbon Dioxide allows heat from the sun to warm the planet, but prevents it from re-radiating back into Space. This concentration compares with about 200 ppm before the industrial revolution, and is down at least in part to man's burning of fossil fuels such as oil and coal and cannot be explained naturally. The warming due to Carbon Dioxide is only part of the problem. Water vapour is by far the most potent of 'greenhouse' gases that acts to warm the atmosphere. And as the concentration of Carbon Dioxide increases, the atmosphere becomes warmer and this warming causes a general increase in the evaporation of our oceans, streams and rivers releasing more water vapour. This vapour causes more warming and the cycle starts to feed back on itself, eventually reaching a point of no return. This area of the science of global warming is known as the runaway greenhouse effect and is the most worrying aspect of all, the idea that we will eventually reach a point whereby the climate changes irreversibly and whatever we do will have no bearing on it.

Studies of a subject called Comparative Planetology are very interesting. This effectively compares the terrestrial planets of Venus, Earth and Mars, all of which began life billions of years ago in similar states and each being of fairly similar sizes, the only difference being Venus was closest to the sun. It turns out that because of Venus's proximity to the sun, evaporation of water from its oceans began quite quickly. This caused further warming because water vapour is a strong greenhouse gas, and the process fed back on itself to the extent that all water on its surface eventually evaporated. Venus now has an atmosphere of Carbon Dioxide and a surface temperature just short of 500 degrees Celsius.

This is not designed to show that Earth is next, but is used as an example of what does happen when planetary conditions enter a runaway greenhouse phase. It is also food for

thought to the very small minority of really quite vocal scientists who rubbish climate change and state that there is no need to curtail our Carbon Dioxide emissions. If they are right and man is having no influence on climate around the world then that is fine and we can all sleep easy. But, if they are wrong like the vast majority of scientists think they are, then we will reach a point, in the not too distant future, when we will have no control over our ever warming climate with its enormous implications for mankind. I don't know about you, but I really don't want to take that sort of risk with our future. This is why we must try and curb Carbon Dioxide emissions as a matter of urgency.

Flood and drought

The science is all well and good, but what does global warming and climate change actually mean to us in our region? I believe we have seen weather patterns over the last ten years that may give us an indication of what could lie ahead. But to explain, we need to move to the tropics and look at a Caribbean hurricane as an example. Such a storm, once

A car crushed by a fallen tree in Woodhouse Lane, Leeds. This incident was newsworthy when it happened back in 1983, but such calamities could well become commonplace if our weather turns angrier as a result of increasingly deep areas of low pressure. *(YPN)*

developed, takes its energy from the warm waters of the tropical sea. It therefore follows that the warmer the sea, the more potentially powerful the hurricane. 2004 was remarkable for the ferocity and frequency of hurricanes. The number that made landfall over the state of Florida has only ever been repeated once before, in the 1880s in Texas. Several were category 5 hurricanes, the most powerful possible. It turns out that the Caribbean sea was on average 1.5 deg C warmer than normal.

Areas of low pressure, or depressions, that affect the British Isles are weaker versions of hurricanes. It thus follows that our areas of low pressure may well become angrier if there is more energy available to them; the deeper the low pressure,

Violent storms of almost tropical intensity are likely to become more common in Yorkshire as a result of climate change. This was graphically illustrated on the evening of June 19, 2005, when a mass of warm air from south of the Azores, which had brought extreme heat and humidity, was destabilised by a cold front coming in from the Atlantic. Freak storms broke out on the western fringe of the North York Moors, with some villages receiving almost three inches of rain — the normal amount for a month — within one hour. Typical of the devastation was the scene at Boltby Reservoir. What would normally be a trickle of water in the overflow channel was turned into a fast-flowing river 100ft wide, with a large chunk of the walling being ripped out and deposited at the foot of the dam. *(Chris Long)*

the heavier the rainfall and the stronger the winds. So we may expect more damage due to strong winds, and more instances of flooding due to heavier rainfall. However our planet cannot and does not consist solely of areas of low pressure. The Earth's atmosphere has to have a balance of pressure systems and so if we have deeper areas of low pressures then we must have – equal and opposite – stronger areas of high pressure. Areas of high pressure give fine and dry weather, and as a general rule the stronger these are, the more persistent they are likely to be - leading to longer periods of dry weather or drought. And so our weather is likely to become schizophrenic and at times swing from one extreme to the other.

Over the past ten years or so, we have experienced some remarkable extremes. These were covered in more detail in *Weather or Not*, but to summarise, in 1995 the spring to late autumn period was incredible for its lack of rainfall. Yorkshire was gripped by a chronic shortage of water, and although a lot of the blame has to be directed at the water authority, they were dealing with a serious drought situation. The most

The flash flooding of June 19, 2005 quickly overwhelmed the Mary Hall Stables at Boltby. The water swept through the yard, leaving a yawning gap where a stable block once stood and sweeping several cars downstream. Anna Bramall starts the massive clean-up operation by rescuing a painting. (*YPN*)

remarkable thing about 1995 was that the traditional wet autumn period failed to bring any noticeable rainfall. The figures show that Scar House Reservoir in Nidderdale experienced a 1 in 500-year rainfall deficit event.

We only need to fast forward five years for the next major weather extreme to hit our area. Autumn 2000 saw Yorkshire and the UK hit by unprecedented rainfall; spring that year was wet, and the land never dried out during the summer months. The River Ouse in York rose to its highest ever June level and caused summer flooding in the city. As September began there was no let up in the rain, its intensity and frequency reaching a crescendo at the end of October and beginning of

Episodes of serious drought may become more common across Yorkshire as our climate continues to change. The period from spring to autumn 1995 was one of the driest on record with Yorkshire gripped with a chronic lack of rainfall for much of the time. At Scar House Reservoir in Nidderdale, statistics show that a rainfall deficit event such as this should occur on average once every 500 years. Persistent areas of high pressure kept the rain-bearing clouds away for long periods of time. Reservoirs such as Thruscross in the Washburn valley (seen here) revealed secrets from the past as their respective water levels fell to incredibly low levels. *(YPN)*

November, causing widespread flooding and misery to thousands of homes across the country. Stockbridge, Keighley, for example suffered the highest concentration of flooded properties anywhere in the country – 325.

What became apparent that year was the near tropical intensity of rainfall that many of us had never seen before in this part of the world. At one stage the A1 was under several feet of water. I remember coming back from York on the A59 after an outside broadcast for *Look North,* driving at 10mph with full wiper speed on and still not being able to see out of the windscreen because of the sheer intensity of the rain. When the statistics were analysed, it tuned out to be a 1 in 500-year rainfall excess event. So within five years the region had experienced two 1 in 500-year events of opposite types.

Rising sea levels

One of the most obvious implications of climate change is rising sea levels. As the Earth becomes warmer, so the seas and oceans will expand. To a lesser extent, the melting of glaciers and mountain snow will also contribute. Current mean estimates put the expected rise in sea levels at about 50cm between now and the end of the century, with a range as low as 15cm and as high as 95cm. Our coastline is also under threat from bigger tidal surges as a result of deeper areas of low pressure. These would cause the sea level to rise further

than normal and create stronger winds, which would in turn cause bigger surges. When these elements combine with a high spring tide, the combination that caused such serious flooding in 1953 to the East Coast is likely to become worse. In the first half of 2005 there were two such surges, one in Hull early in the year being the highest recorded tide since the late 1960s.

Since *Weather or Not* was written there have been more extremes to affect Yorkshire, the UK and Europe.

2003 - the year of drought

The spring, summer and autumn of 2003 will be remembered for years. Just as the summer of 1976 holds vivid memories for heat and sunshine, 2003 will be recalled for its amazing period of dry and sunny weather through March and April. There was also very warm weather in summer, although the really intense heat and new record temperatures were reserved for areas further south. Autumn was largely settled as well, with an abundance of sunshine and increasing lack of

The shape of things to come? Paull nature reserve, near Hull, in June 2005. The notice reads: "Environment Agency. No swimming. Strong currents. No diving. Underwater obstacles." Comments the photographer: "Is this a global warning? Worrying stuff?" *(Bob Carter)*

rainfall. This was the main reason for an amazingly vivid display of colours on our trees, as the hedgerows and bushes teemed with fruits and berries.

Although rainfall in January 2003 was close to average, February (41% of the long term average), March (36%) and April (43%) all had less than half the normal rainfall as high pressure dominated our weather throughout. A close look at the statistics shows that at Waddington, Lincolnshire, exactly the same rainfall fell during the first four months of 1976 as in the same period during 2003. For the first time in living memory, the Bolton Abbey moors in North Yorkshire were closed over the Easter Bank Holiday weekend as they had become tinder dry and represented a seri-

Fork lightning seen looking across to Ilkley Moor during August 2004. This was a stormy month, caused by very humid sub-tropical air, with frequent lightning storms and torrential rain, which caused flooding across many parts of Yorkshire. It was a combination of events that symbolises real concerns about future climate change. *(Tony Ireland)*

ous fire hazard. But it was fabulous news for the tourist industry with record numbers of visitors.

There was some rainfall during the summer months, largely in the form of heavy showers, but drought conditions returned during late summer into autumn. Farmers across Lincolnshire complained that they could not sow their winter wheat because the land was so arid – but again tourism was the big winner. I remember doing an outside broadcast for *Look North* in Bridlington riding a donkey called Peter Levy (don't ask!). Without exaggeration it looked like the Mediterranean and all hotels and guesthouses were full – even the donkey rides were making a fortune as people shunned holidays abroad and decided to stay at home.

As it turned out, the annual rainfall in 2003 was the lowest since the summer of 1975. That summer has been largely forgotten because of the heat and drought of 1976, but it was a beautiful year and in fact the lack of rainfall was the reason for the drought crisis of 1976. This is the reason why there was real concern about water stocks in 2004. There was never any question of problems with supply in 2003, but as in 1975/1976 prolonged dry spells can last for eighteen months – hence the fears for the following year. Our reservoir stocks fell to around 35% in autumn, and this was despite massive

water abstraction from our river network. In the end heavy rainfall came to our rescue during December, and continued into 2004. Yorkshire Water deserves credit for its unique underground system of pipes, which enable water to be pumped around the area and seem to have responded well following the debacle of 1995. Unfortunately, other water companies do not seem to be in such a good position. Indeed, following another very dry winter in 2004/2005, drought orders were issued in southern England.

It was not just Yorkshire, Lincolnshire and the North Midlands that had an extraordinary year in 2003. The UK and Europe as a whole saw records broken on a regular basis. Almost the entire globe was warmer than the 1961 to 1990 climatological average. As the UK broke its temperature record in Kent, Europe continued to swelter in a relentless heat wave. Fires raged across the continent, prompting Pope John Paul the second to urge people to pray for rain. "I invite all to join in my prayers for the victims of this calamity, and I exhort all to raise to the Lord fervent entreaties so that He may grant the relief to the thirsty earth," he said.

At the same time, fire fighters in north-eastern Italy worked for a third day to put out a blaze in the countryside near Udine. Three big fires burned in Portugal. The government asked Spain for two fire-fighting planes to help tackle a wild-fire near Portilimo, in the southern region of the Algarve. By the time the fires had been extinguished, 390,000 hectares of forest and bush land were destroyed, together with 125,000 hectares in Spain. In the French Alps, police warned hikers about avalanches near Mont Blanc, as glacial ice continued to melt, loosening rocks from the mountainside – 44 climbers were rescued because of this danger. In the Bavarian city of Roth the temperature hit 105F, beating the previous record of 104F which was set in 1983. The Mediterranean experienced record sea temperatures of 30C (86F).

According to the United Nations, the hot summer across Europe led to around 20,000 deaths and over $10 billion of agricultural losses. Not as well perceived was the impact on the power trade market. The flow of central European rivers approached all-time low levels in August and September. Remarkably, the River Danube fell to an all-time low only twelve months after it had risen to an all-time high, when devastating floods affected much of Europe. Consequently, several power plants had to reduce their output because they could not divert enough cooling water from the rivers. However, drinking water supplies remained unaffected due to the heavy rainfalls of the previous year.

Averaged across England and Wales, 2003 was the fourth warmest summer since records began 345 years ago. The period March to August was the warmest on record, and the highest maximum temperature in the UK was broken at Faversham, Kent, with 38.5C (100F). Annual rainfall for England and Wales totalled 761mm, which made 2003 the driest year since 1975, with August the sixth driest month on record. It was also the sunniest year since averaged sunshine records began in 1961.

2004 – the year of summer floods

This was a year that really disappointed. In the tenuous land of long-range forecasting the signs were there as 2003 had been very similar to 1975. Such spells of anticyclonic dry weather have been known to last up to eighteen months, leading to the possibility that the spring and summer of 2004 might be good as well. Also, research carried out by Dr Roeder from Berlin University suggested that anticyclonic conditions might well dominate Europe once again. Dr Roeder's method was to look at the pressure patterns across the Northern Hemisphere and compare them with those over the last century. His track record had been very good over the previous twelve months – indeed I bathed in the glory of correct long-range forecasts in 2003 on the back of Dr Roeder! However, our luck was about to run out spectacularly.

Long-range forecasts need to be taken with an enormous pinch of salt. Sometimes we struggle to get tomorrow right, never mind forecasting correctly six months ahead. However, I always take the view that if there is evidence to suggest we are more likely to get a certain type of weather than another, then the viewers would like to know, even if it may well be wrong. With the stick I had during the summer of 2004 I frankly wondered why I bothered opening my mouth but that's another story!

It was with great gusto that I announced on *Look North* in March that the signs were good for spring and summer. Indeed May was a beautiful month, which heightened people's expectations even more. As we entered the early part of June, everything was looking good for a great summer. As early as the second week, temperatures across the country reached 31C (88F) for the first time in early June – yes, you've guessed it – since the summer of 1976. Temperatures in Lincolnshire climbed to 30C (86F).

The mini heat wave broke with an enormous thunderstorm that deposited marble-sized hail in Leven, East Yorkshire. Ironically, this was the first sign of the terrible storms that were to hammer our region later in the summer. June went from bad to worse. An area of low pressure that hit the Lincolnshire Show on the 23rd – with central pressure of 982mb – equalled the lowest ever recorded in the last hundred years. It led to flooding, with over three inches of rain falling in Buxton in forty-eight hours, and the uprooting of trees in the south-west of the country.

July was a very poor month with yet another deep area of low pressure sweeping across our region, again uprooting trees and bringing down power lines. At RAF Wittering four inches of rain was recorded in twenty-four hours, which led to the A1 in north Cambridgeshire being completely flooded. July 2004 at Wittering was the wettest month on record; incredibly, as we will see later, the record was only to last for a month.

August was a terrible month, but very unusual in that tropical air from ex-hurricane Alex made it feel more like the Caribbean than the north of England. For much of the month the air remained very humid. Once Alex's air had been swept away it was replaced by tropical air from ex-hurricane Danielle. In my time at the Met Office in broadcasting it felt as busy as it was during the floods of autumn 2000. Once extreme weather events occur, your time is stretched to the limit with most radio stations and TV bulletins wanting up to date analysis and forecasts.

The high humidities created unprecedented demand at local hospitals for treatment of respiratory problems. Night-time temperatures rarely fell below 16C (61F), and, despite the cloud cover, daytime temperatures regularly reached the mid-seventies. In the early hours of 9th August, following a hot weekend, cloud cover prevented night-time temperatures in some areas from falling to below 21C (70F). Many sites across the region recorded their warmest ever night since records began, a feat shared across the country.

The air felt so high in energy it was bound to end with a thunderstorm. In this country the heat and humidity from the continent usually gives way to fresher weather as a cold front pushes in from the west. Normal service then resumes, but not this time. The wind remained in the south with low pressure close by. The result was incredible. The thunderstorms when they came were the heaviest and most violent that I have ever witnessed in my time in the Met Office. Salandine Nook, just outside Huddersfield, experienced such a storm. One of my ex-colleagues, who had for years been a trained Met Office observer at Stanstead airport, said that it was the worst he had ever experienced. In the end he appeared on *Look North*, speaking on his mobile phone in the middle of the storm live from Milnsbridge, where a wall had collapsed as it was unable to cope with the volume of water flowing off the fields. In about ninety minutes nearly 70mm of rain was recorded from this storm, which caused severe localised flooding. The amazing thing was that flooding of some kind was occurring every day over a two-week period.

Almost as if it had been sent as a punishment, I had no roof during much of August as we were having an extension put on the back of the house. I spent many a night emptying buckets and on some occasions the rain poured in through the makeshift tarpaulin roof. Twice in one week I drove home up the Wetherby road when it was completely flooded and had to mount the kerb and use the grass in the middle of the carriageways.

Sad as it may seem, during a thunderstorm I decided to get footage from my bedroom window. I remember a flash of lightning that seemed very close, but it was only when I played it back and froze the image that I realised it had struck the telephone wire at the bottom of the garden! A lucky escape indeed, as I was in the garden only thirty minutes earlier. Now that really would be a forecaster's nightmare. Death by lightning strike – I somehow think that a lot of people would have found that hilarious!

The list of flooded towns was endless – Newark (101mm in 30 hours), Gainsborough, Beverley, Leeds, York, Pateley Bridge, Scarborough, Filey and many more – all of which received a month's worth of rain in only a few hours, often from separate thunderstorms on different days. The widespread nature of the localised flooding was incredible. The floods that affected Boscastle, Cornwall, on 16th August, fifty-two years to the day since the famous Lynmouth floods occurred, graphically indicated the intensity of the rainfall. The Met Office has calculated that 200mm of rain fell in about five hours as a convergence line developed along the north coast of Cornwall. The images of this flash flood were beamed around the world – a true natural disaster in every sense of the word.

Only a day later, more intense rainfall caused mudslides near Stirling in Scotland. It seemed as though it would be never ending. Gone was the notion that only people who lived close to a river or stream were at risk. The sheer volume of rainfall was such that anyone and everyone became at risk from flooding. The drains, simply unable to cope with the volume of water coming out of the sky, backed up and flooded people's homes.

There were some incredible statistics come the end of August 2004, and it was a great relief that by the Bank Holiday weekend we saw a return to somewhat drier weather conditions. At RAF Wittering, as mentioned earlier, July 2004 was their wettest ever month with records stretching back to the 1950s. Incredibly the record only lasted a matter of weeks as August then beat July to become their wettest ever month. Both months recorded in excess of 160mm, Met Office statistical analysis showing that this has a return period once every 500 years. RAF Leuchars in north-east Scotland recorded 331% of average rainfall, making it the wettest August on record, with data going back to 1922. The Met Office average rainfall across all sites, and for our region, show it was both the wettest August and wettest summer since these type of records began in 1961. So much for my long-range forecasts!

The future

The history books are littered with examples of summer flash floods, heatwaves and general flooding over the centuries. It is also worth noting that it is not possible to say that any one extreme weather event on its own is down to climate change. But the number of extreme weather events, including the contrasting summer weather in 2002 (extreme flood in Europe), 2003 (extreme heat and drought in UK and Europe) and 2004 (floods and excess rainfall in the UK) has stimulated discussions about the possibility that these events are indicators of man-made climate change. Temperature anomalies in Switzerland should occur only in the order of once in several thousand years if our climate is not in fact warming artificially. However, if man is warming our climate, as seems increasingly indisputable, then the hot dry summer across Europe of 2003 will become more frequent, together with episodes of extreme rainfall and flood as we saw across Europe in 2002 and in the UK in August 2004.

As the Earth continues to warm, we can expect our climate to continue to change, swinging from one extreme to another. I prefer the term climate change as opposed to global warming. This I feel gives people the misleading notion that our climate may warm and that is good, because it may mean hotter, drier summers. The only thing that is certain is that our climate will continue to change, and one theory suggests that may not in fact become warmer, drier or wetter. Some scientists are becoming concerned that our climate may change in a very different way to that described above. The UK is on the same latitude as Canada and as such should be much colder than it is now. The only thing that prevents this from happening is the Gulf Stream, which is a huge conveyor of warm water from the Gulf of Mexico that keeps our shores artificially warm. As our planet continues to warm, ice at the North Pole will continue to melt. This fresh water pouring into the Atlantic will change the density of the seawater and cause the Gulf Stream to become cut off in the mid-Atlantic. This would cause our weather to change drastically, becoming much, much colder.

There remain very difficult decisions to be made by governments around the world. Fossil fuel power stations will have to be replaced. Tidal, wind and solar power can all generate electricity without producing Carbon Dioxide, but would be unable on their own to produce enough energy for our needs. As unpalatable as it may seem to many of us, there really is only one alternative capable of producing CO2 free electricity in sufficient quantity, and that is nuclear power. Another major area that would help enormously is energy conservation. Incredibly the vehicles on America's roads consume 11% of the world's energy, and it is no surprise that the USA is responsible for 25% of the entire world's Carbon Dioxide emissions. But little things can make an enormous difference. Energy saving light bulbs use only 20% of the electricity of normal bulbs. Just imagine how much less electricity would be used if every one of us had at least one of these light bulbs in our homes.

A few scientists still do not accept the concept of man-made climate change. Lord May, the distinguished chair of the Royal Society in London, had some strong words for them on Newsnight early in July 2005. He said there is no doubt that man is changing our climate. He was scathing of the press and media, who give equal time to the doubters, even though those who accept the principles of man-made climate change vastly outweigh them. This, he said, has the effect of suggesting to the public that there is a split in the scientific community when there is not. He went on to say that if one looks hard enough then one can find doubters in any science, however absurd their views might be. He gave as examples the few scientists who still believe that HIV does not leads to AIDS, and in years gone by those who argued that smoking was not linked to lung cancer. It cannot be over-emphasised how strong these comments are for an organisation like the Royal Society, which speaks for leading scientists in countries from around the world, and they give an idea of its deep anxiety at what might lie ahead.

Return of Winter

Weather events are increasingly being exacerbated by climate change, but nevertheless every so often there is a 'blip' and the pendulum momentarily swings back the other way. Just when it seemed that significant snowfall was becoming a thing of the past, the period between November 2004 and February 2005 brought a reminder of winters past. We end this book with a look at conditions – sometimes glorious and at others harsh – that will be long remembered. Apart from being something of a throwback, they also restored the faith of those who believe in weather lore.

Berries & Waxwings

Perhaps one of the best known pieces of weather lore is associated with berries on the trees in winter. It is often said that bumper crops of berries in autumn is a sure sign of a harsh winter to follow. Most people will conclude that in fact the trees are only reacting to the weather conditions during the previous spring and summer, and that it is impossible for them to have prior knowledge of the weather that lies ahead. However this could well be missing the point. Just as farmers over the centuries had noticed that a red sky at night can lead to a fine spell of weather, people over the years have concluded that copious berries on the trees has often been a good predictor of cold weather. Could it be that the conditions that have helped produce numerous berries have been followed by a cold winter simply because the weather can and does follow patterns and cycles? Bill Foggitt certainly thought so, and he famously predicted several harsh winters of the last century by making such an observation during the autumn. It

is worth noting that cold, snowy winters were much more common until the 1980s, and so predicting a cold winter was much less risky that it is today!

Bill Foggitt certainly does have one claim to fame that is very difficult to argue against. Having observed an early flock of waxwings during late 1962 he suggested that this was a precursor to a harsh winter to follow. Indeed it turned out that the winter of 1963 was statistically the coldest of the twentieth century. There is some truth to this piece of weather lore. Waxwings are native to Siberia and northern Scandinavia, and when conditions there are very harsh they fly south to find food. Late 2004 was another occasion when waxwings were spotted, first in north-east Scotland and then at Bempton Cliffs near Flamborough. This did not necessarily mean we were going to get cold weather. An east or north-easterly wind is needed to bring the cold air towards us, but flocks of waxwings can at least give an indication that harsh cold weather is to the north-east of us and so not that far away meteorologically.

So did the bumper crop of berries and the sightings of waxwings lead to a cold winter in 2004/2005? The jury is out on that one. Compared with the cold winters before the 1980s, this one hardly registers. However it is fair to say that we did have several outbreaks of cold air from the north and the east, the later one in February leading to the heaviest snowfall since 1995. Such is our climate at the moment that January was the mildest for fifteen years and the relatively high ground temperatures meant the snow thawed rapidly. But there was at least some wintry weather. Next time we see a bumper crop of berries, together with large flocks of waxwings, it will be interesting to see what winter brings.

Waxwings feeding on berries in the Sheffield area. The weatherman Bill Foggitt believed that early flocks were a sure sign of a harsh winter to follow. *(Andy Jones)*

Bumper crops of berries are said to be another sign of a hard winter to come. This was certainly the case in 2004 when many trees had berries in abundance ahead of the heaviest snowfall for ten years. These photographs of rowan (left) and holly (above) were taken in Hebden Gill, Upper Wharfedale. *(David Joy)*

(Opposite, top) There was a rare early taste of winter in November 2004 with a blast of icy cold air from the Arctic. This picture was taken at Winscar reservoir in South Yorkshire, near the village of Dunford Bridge. The clear blue sky and excellent visibility is the hallmark of a winter northerly in Pennine areas. The old weather lore saying, 'Ice in November to bear a duck, the rest of the winter nowt but slush and muck', didn't work on this occasion. The region was affected by two more outbreaks of cold and snow later in the winter, albeit only briefly. *(Phil Hartley)*

(Lower) Another memorable winter picture, again taken during the Arctic blast of November 2004 showing Scammonden dam surrounded by the snow-covered hills of Kirklees and Calderdale. *(Roger Lockwood)*

(This page) A brave walker on the way to Ingleborough summit on Boxing Day 2004. The weather was breathtaking, a clean north to north-westerly giving crystal clear visibility and a beautiful blue sky. Note the snow drifting down the side; a scene more akin to the Alps than the Yorkshire Dales! *(Nigel Baker)*

Dreaming of a white Christmas

A white Christmas is another increasingly rare part of our climate. That is, a proper white Christmas, with snow on the ground as depicted by many a Christmas card, as opposed to the slightly artificial technical version, which allows for one flake of snow in the twenty-four hour period of Christmas Day. I remember working one particular Christmas night shift, and at 11pm we had a heavy shower in Leeds. Our observer at the time, who will remain nameless, swears blind that he saw one flake of snow during a particularly heavy shower that hour. He reported it as a sleet shower to headquarters, with the end result that Leeds weather centre made headlines the next day as one of the locations that had experienced a white Christmas. Now I'm not saying it wasn't a sleet shower, but it is amazing what odds of 8 to 1 and a Christmas sherry or two can do to one's eyesight!

Anyone who longs for snow on the ground over Christmas would be rather jealous of how often it was recorded during the very much colder winters of the past. Between 1782 and 1821 there were sixteen white Christmases in forty years. Charles Dickens observed six before he reached the age of thirty. In 1860 the whole country was buried under an 'enormous' snowfall. On Christmas Day 1927, sixteen-foot drifts cut off many towns and villages. 1970 was a year with good falls of prolonged snow, and interestingly 1976 was a white Christmas (this year famously went on to be a scorching summer that many people long for again!).

The only 'proper' one that I remember was 1981, although it didn't snow on Christmas Day itself. However, six to twelve inches of snow lay on the ground which made it a memorable sledging Christmas in Keighley! We paid the price for this heavy cover of snow with widespread flooding early in 1982 as seen elsewhere in the book.

More recently we have been quite lucky in that, although the winters have become milder and milder, we have had three official white Christmases: In 1999, live on Look North, I famously predicted snow seven days before the event. The next day I went to work and felt sick when the forecast had changed dramatically from a cold northerly to a strong, mild south-westerly. I was inundated with calls from people saying they had put money on at the bookies and that I would be in trouble if I was wrong! For the next five days the forecast remained the same and I was about to throw in the towel. It then miraculously reverted back to a cold northerly and it snowed between 8am and 9am on Christmas morning. What a relief! I am convinced that someone was looking down on me that Christmas. 1995 was another year and, as the photographs on these pages suggest, 2004 saw snow falling on 25th December across much of the region.

Solutions to 'Linked Town Names' on page 18

1.	Live and Let Live	16.	No news is good news
2.	Too slow to catch cold	17.	The long arm of the law
3.	Three men in a tub	18.	What a gay day
4.	Some you win some you lose	19.	Brass monkey weather
5.	As far as the eye can see	20.	One man and his dog
6.	Spring is in the air	21.	A red under the bed
7.	A fish out of water	22.	Peter Pan and Tinker Bell
8.	Give it a whirl	23.	Little Red Riding Hood
9.	Horse muck for your rose bush	24.	The good, the bad and the ugly
10.	Wet behind the ears	25.	A bird in hand is worth two in the bush
11.	Has the cat got your tongue?	26.	Hit the road Jack
12.	Bread board and butter dish	27.	Fall apart at the seam
13.	A mug of hot cocoa	28.	The point of no return
14.	Water off a duck's back	29.	Feeling the pinch
15.	Wait on hand and foot	30.	A happy Christmas and a happy New Year

(Above) The Peak District looked just as wintry and windswept as the Yorkshire Dales on Boxing Day 2004. Its tallest peak, Mam Tor, towers above the village of Castleton in the valley below. *(Andy Jones)*

(Lower) Another fabulous photograph from Boxing Day 2004, this time of Leeming reservoir, Oxenhope. As perfect a winter's day as we could ever hope for in this country. *(Arthur Leng)*

What direction for our future weather? *(Anna Gowthorpe)*

(Left Above) The thickest of the snow has melted away on Malham Moor, but enough was left to make this spectacular picture. It was taken from the viewer's 'back yard' on Chapel Fell looking towards Malham Tarn. *(Bernadette Schutte)*

(Left Lower) The Yorkshire Wolds near Thixendale. This part of Yorkshire is particularly prone to snow with an unstable northerly bringing showers down the East Coast. One such shower can be seen approaching from the north, seconds away from obscuring the sun and dumping more heavy snow on the area. *(Anna Gowthorpe)*

(Right Above) It is a long time since snow blowers were used in Yorkshire. But after the prolonged heavy snow that affected the North York Moors in February 2005, they were the only machine that could even attempt to clear the road at Blakey Ridge. *(Graham Ward)*

(Right Lower) An incredible scene from February 2005 reminiscent of much harsher winters from the middle of last century. This is the direct route from the photographer's house to the main Swaledale road. The drift blocking the entire single-track lane is 4ft 6in deep. He commented, "The drift is too deep for our Land Rover Defender and we are now 'sitting it out' and waiting for a big thaw or Highways to come and dig us out. Not sure how much of a priority we are but they have been notified by e-mail'. How times have changed! Within a week the snow had all but thawed. In winter's gone by, it would have lasted until spring. *(Jeremy Hutchinson)*